# GOD

— OR —

# SCIENCE?

## Is Science Denying God?

# GOD
## OR
# SCIENCE?
### Is Science Denying God?

Antonino Del Popolo

*University of Catania, Italy*

 **World Scientific**

NEW JERSEY · LONDON · SINGAPORE · BEIJING · SHANGHAI · HONG KONG · TAIPEI · CHENNAI · TOKYO

*Published by*

World Scientific Publishing Co. Pte. Ltd.

5 Toh Tuck Link, Singapore 596224

*USA office:* 27 Warren Street, Suite 401-402, Hackensack, NJ 07601

*UK office:* 57 Shelton Street, Covent Garden, London WC2H 9HE

**British Library Cataloguing-in-Publication Data**
A catalogue record for this book is available from the British Library.

**GOD OR SCIENCE?**
**Is Science Denying God?**

ISBN 978-981-125-872-5 (hardcover)
ISBN 978-981-126-558-7 (paperback)
ISBN 978-981-125-873-2 (ebook for institutions)
ISBN 978-981-126-026-1 (ebook for individuals)

For any available supplementary material, please visit
https://www.worldscientific.com/worldscibooks/10.1142/12901#t=suppl

Desk Editor: Rhaimie Wahap

Typeset by Stallion Press
Email: enquiries@stallionpress.com

# CONTENTS

# INTRODUCTION

*"Religion without science is blind,*
*science without religion is lame."*

— A. Einstein

In the Metamorphoses, Ovid wrote

*"... man had as a gift a face turned upwards and his gaze aims*
*at the sky and rises towards the stars..."*

This sentence highlights, with great force, one of the main characteristics of the human being: his desire to know, bringing him to ask questions about the world around him, about the meaning of life and death, about the origin and end of the Universe and life. I like to imagine a primitive man not yet fully erect, with the palm of one hand resting on the ground, and with an inquisitive face and eyes turned upward, curious and bewildered by all those lights that fill the sky. A hand on the ground, *humus*, a term etymologically similar to *homo*, man, and eyes to the sky: man is a sort of bridge between the Earth, which generated him, and the Universe father of all things. Centuries and millennia have not changed this peculiar characteristic of man to question himself about what surrounds him. Among the first questions that children ask us is where does what surrounds us come from? who did it? where do we come from? Every being on Earth has a genetic code and it seems that in that of the human being there are written these questions that arise from a limitless curiosity, which seeks and when it finds it continues to search. The questions we ask ourselves as children, become more pressing and more precise as we grow up. It is natural to ask ourselves not only where the Universe came from, but why it exists. Why is there something rather than nothing? Who architected reality and why does it show itself as we see it and not in a different way? What's the point of all this? You can answer as Bertrand Russell did "The Universe just exists" and thus close the discussion. However, this has not happened in history. To try to solve these questions, the mankind brightest minds have tried their hand at different paths but without reaching tangible conclusions. The attempt to solve these dilemmas has pushed man in different directions: towards religion, towards philosophy, and more recently towards science. These are the three fundamental ways under which those questions have been pondered in the hitherto vain attempt to unravel them. Yet, these paths don't have much in common, apart from the ultimate goal: to understand reality.

The confidence of scientists that these problems could be part of science is linked to the great development that cosmology has undergone, especially in the past decades, and to the ever-growing understanding of the microscopic world.

Philosophy deals with studying, using logic, the real and the ideal with the ultimate purpose to understand their nature and the ultimate purpose of things. Since the times of Plato and Aristotle, philosophy was understood as the search for the origin of the world and what made it up. For millennia, philosophy has been regarded as the repository of true knowledge. In the *Doctrine of Science*, the philosopher Fichte went in search of a *science of science*. In such research, the role of science was diminished and reduced to a simple practical function. However, the overbearing development of science has denied this point of view by relegating philosophy to the *mother of other sciences*, in Bacon's vision.

Science tries to explain or predict the results of experiments, to understand what reality is made of, how it originated and what future it has. Unlike religion and philosophy, which are also driven by the desire to find explanations for our fundamental questions, science follows a method, a triple thread connection between observation, experiments and theory.

Religion, on the other hand, is based on truths revealed by supreme beings or their prophets that must be believed without the possibility of verification, verification that it is instead the central point of science. As Galileo often repeated, *"Scripture does not teach us how Heaven goes, but how we go to Heaven"*. Copernicanism took away the centrality of the Earth, it showed a world in which the role of human beings was much more limited than what was previously believed. It wiped out the Aristotelian-Ptolemaic universe, and with it, broke Augustine's Christian vision of the universe, created starting from the Aristotelian-Ptolemaic model itself. Copernicanism was not only a change of direction in the vision of the cosmos, but a sort of first secularization, extended by Darwinism and by the discoveries that science made in the following centuries. When the reins of science were released, this like a runaway horse opened new paths and brought new knowledge that restricted the spaces of religion and philosophy. Nonetheless, it took centuries before it was realized that science could have a life of its own, not dependent on faith. Again, for Galileo, a world without God would have risked, similarly to what would happen to science without the mathematical language, to *"wander in vain through a dark labyrinth"*. In one of the dialogues with Bentley, concerning the nature of gravity, Newton assumed that there must be a *"material or immaterial agent"* that produced it. In other words, in Newton's mind, hovered the specter that in order to support an infinite Universe, an equally infinite God, who permeated the space, was needed to keep its structure intact.

The so-called *physical theology* or *natural theology*, distinct from *revealed theology*, based on scriptures, sought in the natural field, arguments supporting the existence of God. In it, the natural course followed, like the water of a river, the riverbed designed by the creator, the will of the creator who regulates creation with constant and continuous effects. Although its origins date back to the Old Testament and to Greek philosophy, it had a shining period from the end of the 17th century to Darwin. Just to mention some of its proponents, Raymond of Sabunde, and William Paley, wrote books on the evidence of the existence of God from the manifestations of nature. The latter introduced the *analogy of the watchmaker*, a teleological argument that highlights the need for a builder for each construction.

Malthus himself dedicated the final two chapters of his famous work *Essay on the Population* to Natural Philosophy, and before him Leibniz had coined another term in place of natural philosophy, namely *theodicy*. Even after the publication of Darwin's work on the transmutation of species, the debate on the applicability of teleological ideas to science continued. There were several detractors of the theory: Hume Kant, Kierkegaard, but the arguments that most shook the framework of natural theology were those of Darwin. All species originated from a slow evolutionary process, freeing God from the need to create creatures one by one. Natural philosophy and its teleological aspect has survived to the present time. An example is the so-called argument of the *intelligent design*, much advocated in the United States or as John Polkinghorne writes

> So where is natural theology today, two centuries after William Paley? The short answer is, "Alive and well, having learned from past experience to lay claim to insight rather than to coercive logical necessity, and to be able to live in a friendly relationship with science, based on complementarity rather than rivalry.

Today, cosmological, physical, biological, and chemical narratives push part of science to believe that the Universe was generated without a creator to assist it in its origin and formation. If most scientists see in the Big Bang the act that marked the origin of everything from nothing, it was initially seen as a sort of scientific prop to Genesis. Einstein himself after a lecture by Lemaitre, on the primordial atom, (i.e., the Big Bang) said to him: "*This is the most beautiful and satisfying explanation of creation that I have ever heard*", meaning by "creation", the creation told in the bible.

Taking it to its extreme consequences, many scientists (Hawking, Krauss, etc.) today believe that the Big Bang is the moment of creation and consequently implies a beginning of things from nothing without the need for the intervention of a creator. This idea is obviously in contradiction with religious thought, and common sense (see the watchmaker's argument already cited) according to which "*nothing is created out of nothing*" as already claimed by Parmenides of Elea in the sixth century BC. In fact, one must be careful with the words that are used as the nothingness of physics is not the nothingness of common sense. In physics when we talk about nothing, we refer to the quantum vacuum, the minimum energy of quantum fields. The idea of a universe that comes from nothing is based on the observation that its energy, given by the sum of the positive energy of matter and the negative energy of gravitational fields, is zero! And if no energy is needed to generate the Universe, it can be seen as "*the ultimate free meal*", in the words of Alan Guth.

This is in accordance with the theory of inflation, which represents, always quoting the words of Guth, one of its builders, the "*Bang of the Big Bang*". In this phase, close to the initial moment, the Universe underwent a huge and crazy expansion that took it from infinitesimal dimensions, much smaller than those of an atomic nucleus, to a few centimeters. A certain part of physicists accept the idea that the universe originated from nothing, or as already said more precisely from a fluctuation of the quantum vacuum.

The idea was first published by Edward Tryon in 1973 in *Nature*, but Pascual Jordan had suggested the idea several years earlier, arguing that the vacuum energy is zero due to the cancellation of the negative energy of the gravitational field and the positive one of mass and as a consequence, in his opinion, a star could originate from quantum transitions without violating the conservation of energy. Today, approximate forms of *quantum gravity*, the theory that marries gravity and quantum mechanics, show that the Universe originated from nothing through *quantum tunneling*, as shown by Vilenkin. Obviously, we need to understand what is meant by nothing and in Vilenkin's case the "nothing" would be the absence of space-time, which is not the "absolute nothing".

A Universe that originates randomly from nothing is bad news for religion, which while can accept creation from nothing, cannot accept the absence of the watchmaker. From here were born and continue to be born clashes between these two opposing views of the world.

Religion makes use of the argument of the intrinsic order of the Universe which refers to a being who created order. Despite the discoveries of deterministic chaos by the physics, or the indeterminism of the quantum world, when we look at the complex structures, the organisms that fill the world, with their internal order fighting for survival against the second law of thermodynamics, we are perplexed. How did the observed order originate from quantum chaos, not only in living forms, but also in the Universe itself? Following Bergson there seems to be a creative evolution from which increasingly complex things emerge up to the manifestation of the spirit, while for Teilhard de Chardin evolution is a sort of stochastic process that proceeds by trial and error based on "*oriented randomness*". In a similar way, Ruiz de la Pena thinks of a Universe in which God lets matter explore all the possibilities, of which only one is finally realized. Despite the uncertainty, in some way, God would be the director behind the scenes. Another possibility is that the evolutionary design was generated without a Creator.

Brandon Carter's *anthropic principle* (which we will discuss in the next chapters) is linked to these philosophical disquisitions, introducing finalism into the scientific debate. Physical constants appear to be finely determined for the emergence of life. Famous physicists like Paul Davies and Martin Reese have realized that the Universe appears to have been designed for life. The constants present in our Universe, such as the masses of the various particles, the intensity of the various forces seem to have been fixed so that we could appear on Earth. Minor changes in some of these constants would lead to a completely different Universe in which we would not be present. In other words, we are in a Universe that allows life to exist. For this to happen a *fine-tuning of the constants* is necessary, i.e., that the constants are subject to a "*fine tuning*". In general, fine-tuning is a problem that arises when, in order to reproduce reality, it is necessary to set the *initial conditions* and parameters of a theory with excessive precision.

Physicists with religious inclinations have claimed that this fine-tuning of constants is proof of the existence of a creator. Other physicists or philosophers have proposed the existence of a *"vital principle"*, in the words of Bergson's *Creative Evolution*, the *"elan vital"*, the vital impulse that pushed from one evolutionary line to another until reaching Homo Sapiens and consciousness. Other scientists have eliminated the problem of fine-tuning with the introduction of the multiverse, an infinite number of universes. A creator is no longer needed because statistically in at least one of the universes of the multiverse the constants have the values necessary for life to develop.

These ideas agree with those of Jaques Monod, who in *Chance and necessity* argued that the origin of life and its evolution are only the result of chance.

In his words:

> ... *man knows at last that he is alone in the universe's unfeeling immensity, out of which he emerged only by chance. His destiny is nowhere spelled out, nor is his duty. The kingdom above or the darkness below: it is for him to choose.*

If so, the dispute between science and faith would end, with a winner: science. In reality, much of the knowledge, and especially the cosmological ones, which led to this conclusion is based on speculation: they cannot and perhaps will be never possible to proove them. The cosmology of the early Universe before $10^{-12}$ s is not supported by experimental evidence. It is based on hypotheses that to be verified would require particle accelerators of enormous dimensions between those of the solar system and the galaxy.

Jim Peebles Nobel Prize in Physics in 2019, one of the greatest living cosmologists said that

> *It's very unfortunate that one thinks of the beginning whereas in fact, we have no good theory of such a thing as the*

*beginning.... We don't have a strong test of what happened earlier in time*

In this text we will discuss what the progress of science and the most current knowledge can make us say about the science, religion dispute. The main question we will ask ourselves is whether science has succeeded in making God die, and to be able to say, forcing the meaning of the words of Friedrich Nietzsche *"God is dead! God remains dead! And we killed him"*.

# CHAPTER 1

# BETWEEN COSMOGONIES AND SCIENCE

*"Scientific beliefs are supported by*
*evidence, and they get results. Myths*
*and faiths are not and do not."*

— R. Dawkins

## 1.1 Cosmogonies

The questions about how the universe originated and how it will end is probably as old as human civilization. The answers to these questions have been linked for millennia to mysticism and religions. Ignorance of natural events led men to create myths, to invent gods who oversaw every aspect of life. Each civilization has created its own myths of the creation of the world, all more or less similar. Generally, in them there is a creative divinity, who generates order from chaos. These myths were sacred stories, which were believed blindly, and were passed down from generation to generation.

With the evolution of research and scientific thought, the epesegetic role of divinities and myths has slowly decreased over time. Despite the developments of philosophy and with them of some scientific ideas (e.g., Pythagoras, Archimedes, Anaximander, Empedocles, Aristarchus), it took millennia for a scientific worldview to be consolidated. Many centuries after the introduction of scientific ideas by the Greeks, even Kepler believed that the planets were sentient beings. Descartes and Newton believed that the universe regulated itself by following the laws created by God, but at the same time they believed that God could change them at any moment. Newton believed that God was constantly intervening to make the planets follow the right orbits.

There are myriads of eschatologies, doctrines aimed at investigating the destiny of the individual, of mankind and of the universe. We mention only a few.

1. In a Chinese myth, it is said that darkness reigned supreme at the beginning of time, and the world was an egg containing chaos. Yin and Yang combined so well that Pangu, a giant with two large horns, was born inside the egg. The giant Pangu, slept and grew in the egg. One day he woke up and broke the shell with an ax. The heavier part that constituted it went down to form the Earth and the lighter part rose to form the sky. The giant did not allow heaven and earth to come together and for this he pushed the sky up with his head and the earth down with his feet. Pangu was aided in this effort by four legendary animals: the tortoise, the phoenix, the unicorn and the dragon. At his death his parts gave rise to parts of our universe: the left eye became the Sun and the right eye formed the Moon, his hair the stars of the sky, his breath originated the wind, his sweat originated the rain, while his horns and his body formed the mountains and his veins formed the paths and roads. This was how Pangu created the world.

2. According to the Babylonians, the Universe, empty and black, was inhabited by dragons. Marduk, the strongest of the gods, was equipped with a sword and beams of lightning. One day Marduk met the dragon Tiamat, who boldly blocked his way. Tiamat rushed towards Marduk who captured him in a net of light and with the sword split him in two. He hung high the monster's spotted back, and it became the sky. The belly of the monster became the earth with its rivers and oceans.

3. For the Egyptians, originally eight creatures swam in the Chaos. The males had the head of a frog and the females that of a snake. By merging they generated the Great Egg, which hatched after a very long time. When this happened, the creator appeared, the Sun god, regarded as the father and mother of everything. The two halves of the shell separated the waters of chaos and the Sun

transformed them into the world. Feeling alone, the Sun wanted to inhabit the new world with other beings. His thoughts became the gods and all the other things of the world, while his words gave life to the Earth, and to its creatures.

4. In Greek mythology, in the beginning chaos reigned. Gaea, mother of the Earth, appeared, and generated Uranus, the sky, and Pontus, the primordial sea. Uranus and Gaea generated a lineage of Titans, one of which, Cronus (time), wounded Uranus and took its place. Cronus continued the work of creation and also generated Zeus, who killed Cronus by generating a new kingdom.

Coming to the Jews, the Bible's Genesis has many points in common with parts of the many origin stories. It might seem strange to associate ancient myths with the Genesis of the Bible, the sacred book of Jews and Christians, but it must be remembered that even ancient myths were considered as sacred stories. At the same time, Genesis differs from the mythical cosmogonies of the past. In these, God was part of the matter of which the Universe was made up. In Genesis we speak of a God who creates the Universe independently of the Universe itself.

In Genesis, various points similar to the other mythological tales are recognized: darkness, chaos, etc.:

*In the beginning God created the heaven and the earth. And the earth was without form, and void; and darkness was upon the face of the deep. And the Spirit of God moved upon the face of the waters. And God said, Let there be light: and there was light.*

As is well known, in Genesis it is told how God created the world from nothing in seven days. The authenticity and historicity of Genesis were not questioned until the Protestant Reformation. Furthermore, with the birth of humanism, an attitude developed tending to read ancient texts critically. The Catholic authors continued in the tradition, that is, in considering Genesis as a historical text. The Enlightenment opened a new phase. Among the various scientists Lenormat should be remembered. He began a study of the problem of the relationship between the first chapters of Genesis and the traditions of the Eastern peoples. He concluded against the historicity of Genesis. With a few exceptions (Loisy, a Catholic priest who denied the historical character of the first chapter of Genesis) there was a unanimous Catholic reaction against Lenormat. Leo XIII in the encyclical *Providentissimus Deus* condemned attributing a mythological character to biblical stories and therefore denying their historicity. Today, there are three different ways of looking at things:

1. Genesis is a long allegory with a religious background
2. Some things must be interpreted literally, others not.
3. Fundamentalist attitude (fostered by Evangelicals and Jehovah's Witnesses): the whole bible must be interpreted literally.

This latest idea has been made a reality. Near Cincinnati, there is the Ark Encounter, a park of fundamentalist Christians where events described in the bible and described as historical events are presented.

From the scientific point of view, it is clear that the Genesis account is not credible. To make it more acceptable, it would be necessary to think that the various days represent long periods of time, such as geological eras. Moreover, Genesis is not free from inconsistencies. Just to give an example, verse 1, 3 reports that the light was created on the first day, verses 1, 14–19 report that the Sun and the Moon and the stars (i.e., the light) were created on the fourth day. This is not the only inconsistency in the text. It is evident that the errors present are linked to a human editing carried out by different hands, without a final revision and correction.

In what follows, we will discuss the *genesis described by science*, and then establish in the next chapters how realistic this description is:

### INTERLUDE 1

### POWERS OF TEN

In order to write in a simpler and more compact way large and small numbers, scientists use the powers of 10 notation. A power of 10 is the number followed by a number of zeros equal to the exponent. For example, If we want to write 1000, that is 1 followed by 3 zeros, we will write $10^3$. The mass of the Sun is $2 \times 10^{30}$ kg, that is, 2 followed by 30 zeros: 2000000000000000000000000000000.

In case of small numbers, for example a thousandth, 1/1000 = 0.001, namely 1 preceded by 3 zeros we write: $10^{-3}$

*In summary: $10^n$ stands for 1 followed by n zeros. While $10^{-n}$ stands for 1 preceded by n zeros.*

### MASS UNITS USED IN ASTROPHYSICS

The masses of celestial objects are generally large. The mass of the Sun in kilograms is $2 \times 10^{30}$ and is often used as a unit of measurement for the masses and is written as 1 $M_\odot$

Then: 1 $M_\odot = 2 \times 10^{30}$ kg

A star with a mass 8 times greater than that of the Sun will be indicated as 8 $M_\odot$

### DISTANCE UNITS IN ASTROPHYSICS

Similarly to the masses, distances in astrophysics are expressed in different units:

*Astronomical unit*: indicated by A.U., is the Earth-Sun distance, $\approx$ 149 597 870 700 km

*Light Year*: indicated with l.y., is the distance covered in one year by the light: 9 460 730 472 581 km

*Parsec*: indicated with pc, is equal to 3.26 light years, that is $3.26 \times 10^{16}$ m. Parsec multiples are: kiloparsec, (kpc, 1000 pc); megaparsec (Mpc, $10^6$ pc), and gigaparsec (Gpc, $10^9$ pc).

### TEMPERATURE AND ENERGY UNITS

In this book, temperatures are measured in degrees Kelvin, and indicated with K. To obtain the temperatures in degrees Celsius, °C, one has just to subtract from the value of the temperature in Kelvin the quantity 273.16.

As a measure of energy, we will use electronvolt, eV, and its multiples: kiloelectron-volt (keV, 1000 eV), Megalectronvolt (MeV, $10^6$ eV), Gigaelectronvolt (GeV, $10^9$ eV), the Teraelectronvolt (TeV, $10^{12}$ eV).

*The electronvolt can also be expressed in terms of the Kelvin temperature: $1\ eV \approx 11600\ K$.*

The mass of an object may be expressed in electronvolt and its multiples. For example the mass of the proton $m_p = 1.67 \times 10^{-27}\ kg \approx 938\ MeV/c^2$.

## 1.2 A Brief History of the Big Bang Theory

The conception of the cosmos from antiquity to the Middle Ages and beyond was based on Aristotelian physics and Ptolemy's astronomical models. This Universe was static, nothing changed: the planets and stars moved following immutable and eternal cycles. The idea of stillness was so hard to die that we had to wait until the twentieth century to see a real change. The idea of a static universe was shared by 20th-century scientists, including Einstein (before Hubble's discovery of the expansion of the universe). Two years after the publication of his treatise on the Theory of General Relativity, in 1917, Einstein applied it to the Universe and found results that contradicted his prejudices and those of his time: that is, the static nature of the Universe. He found that his equations predicted an expanding or contracting Universe. Following the generalized prejudice that the Universe was static, he introduced a constant in his equations, the *cosmological constant* $\Lambda$, which acting repulsively countered the gravitational attraction and caused the Universe could remain static.

In 1922, the Russian meteorologist and physicist-mathematician Friedmann published an article in which he showed that the solutions of the equations of General Relaivity applied to the Universe provided three different solutions. The solutions of the Friedmann equations, i.e., the possible types of Universe that the equations describe, are of three types, as shown in Figure 1.1. The three types of universes, i.e. the solutions of Einstein's equations, depend on the density of mass-energy (remember that mass and energy are two sides of the same coin as shown by Einstein with his famous formula $E = mc^2$) of the Universe. It is easy to identify a particular value of the density called critical density, $\rho_c$, whose value is equal to $8.6 \times 10^{-30}$ g/cm$^3$, i.e., 0.00000000000000000000000000000 86 g/cm$^3$, or more simply 5 hydrogen atoms per cubic meter. This density takes this name because it discriminates between the three different types of geometry of the universe plotted in Figure 1.1. In the vertical axis of Figure 1.1, the so-called

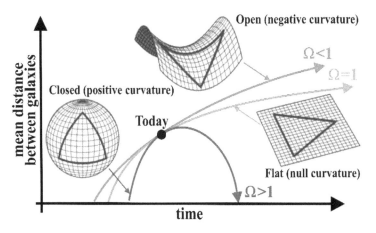

Figure 1.1.   Friedman's universes.

*expansion parameter* is shown which represents the relative expansion of the Universe and can be considered as the average distance between galaxies. In the horizontal axis we have time. If the average density of the universe, $\rho$, is greater than the critical one, $\rho_c$ ($\rho > \rho_c$) the universe expands to a maximum and then collapses again, as seen in the red curve of Figure 1.1. Space is similar to a three-dimensional sphere, and for this reason the spatial geometry of the universe is called *spherical*. This universe is called a *closed universe*, and it has a positive curvature. The curvature indicates how much a curve or an object deviates from being flat. Unlike Euclidean geometry, in this Universe the sum of the internal angles of a triangle is greater than 180°, space is finite and two parallel lines converge. If $\rho < \rho_c$, as seen in the green curve of Figure 1.1, the Universe will expand forever, and for this reason we speak of an *open universe* with negative curvature. Spatial geometry is called *hyperbolic*, and space is infinite. In hyperbolic geometry the sum of the internal angles of a triangle is less than 180° and two parallel lines diverge. If $\rho = \rho_c$, as in the blue line of Figure 1.1, the Universe will expand forever, the geometry is the *Euclidean* one, in which the sum of the internal angles of a triangle are 180° and in this geometry two parallel lines do not meet. The curvature of such a universe is zero. This type of Universe is also called *flat* as the geometry is like that of a plane.

In cosmology, for practical reasons, instead of using the critical density, $\rho_c$, we use the ratio between the density $\rho$ and the critical one, $\rho_c$, and the ratio is called the *density parameter* and is indicated with $\Omega = \rho/\rho_c$. The three types of geometry we saw earlier and shown in Figure 1.1 can be expressed in terms of the density parameter $\Omega$, thus: the flat Universe, with density equal to the critical one ($\rho = \rho_c$) has $\Omega$ equal to one ($\Omega = 1$); the hyperbolic one $\Omega$ less than one ($\Omega < 1$) and the closed one has $\Omega$ greater than one ($\Omega > 1$).

The extent of Friedman's results, and the foundations of the Big Bang theory, are due to a Jesuit presbyter, George Lemaitre who was born in Charleroi in 1894. In 1925 he unknowingly found Friedman's solutions of the equations of General Relativity. He learned that they had already been obtained by Friedman in his meeting with Einstein at the famous Solvay Congress of 1927.

In the same year Lemaitre published one of his articles in an obscure Belgian magazine, which after a few years became famous. Among the results of the work is the relationship between the speed of recession of the extragalactic nebulae, and the distance at which they are located, now known as *Hubble's Law*. Lemaitre's article went unnoticed for 3 years, and it gained notoriety only after being translated into English in 1931.

Hubble's law was experimentally determined in 1929 by Edwin Hubble. Hubble showed that there was a relationship between the recession speeds of galaxies, $v$, and their distance, $r$: $v = Hr$. The quantity $H$ is known as the *Hubble constant* and represents the expansion rate of the Universe.

The definitive acceptance of the Big Bang theory came with the chance discovery of the *Cosmic Microwave Background Radiation* (CMB).

The Cosmic Microwave Background Radiation constitutes the third pillar of the Big Bang theory. It was discovered in 1965 and is a sort of residual microwave sea that pervades the universe and reaches the Earth from all over the sky. A real imprint of the Big Bang. It was predicted in 1948 by Alpher, Herman and Gamow, and its temperature, now known to be 2.725 K, is very close to the value obtained by Alpher and Herman in 1950.

Today, most physicists accept the idea that the Universe was born from the Big Bang, that is, from a singularity of space and time, a sort of non-place and non-time from which what surrounds us originated. However, there are alternative models without singularities (e.g., the *ecpirotic model*) about which we will speak in the following.

Although the Big Bang is not the only theory that describes how the universe originated, it is certainly the one with the most data supporting it, the most accepted and popular.

## Summary: Key points

- Until the 20th century it was believed that the Universe was static. This prompted Einstein to modify the equations of general relativity, which predicted an expanding and contracting universe so that it was static. Friedmann recalculated the solutions of the equations and found that the universe was not static, a result confirmed by Lemaitre. The latter proposed the model of the primordial atom, that is what is now called the Big Bang theory.
- In 1929, Hubble showed, by means of observations, that the universe was not static but expanding.
- Gamow's prediction of the abundance of elements and the *cosmic background radiation* from Penzias and Wilson gave more solid foundations to the Big Bang theory.

# CHAPTER 2

# THE GENESIS ACCORDING TO SCIENCE

*"The mystery of the beginning of the
Universe is insoluble for us".*

— Charles Darwin

Today we are quite certain that our Universe originated 13.8 billion years ago and was very different from what it is today and is expanding in an accelerated way. If we suppose to reverse the expansion motion, as is done when rewinding a movie, what we would expect would be to see the galaxies reverse their motion and all begin to move towards one point. Going back in time, the Universe would become smaller and warmer, reaching temperatures so high that matter, as we know it today, did not exist. We would arrive at a point, when the Universe was $10^{-35}$ m in size, the *Planck era*, in which the laws of known physics would no longer apply. At smaller scales we need a theory that still does not exist: *quantum gravity* which is a combination of the theory of gravity and Quantum Mechanics. Starting from Planck's time, known physics allows us to describe the most important phases of the evolution of the universe. It is of fundamental importance to remember that in any case the discussions relating to the previous $10^{-12}$ s period are essentially speculations, as we will see better in chapter 5. Now we will talk about it a bit.

## 2.1 The Early Universe

About 14 billion years ago the universe had infinitesimal dimensions and it contained all the matter and energy that make it up today. As already mentioned, there is a wall beyond which our theoretical knowledge of the Universe stops. This is the Planck time corresponding to $10^{-43}$ s, characterized by pressures, temperatures ($10^{33}$ K[1]) and density ($10^{96}$ g/cm$^3$) so high that the space is distorted, folded and made up of a foam of mini black holes and *wormholes* (sort of gravitational tunnels) with dimensions of the order of $10^{-33}$ cm, temperatures of $10^{32}$ K and evaporation times of the order of Planck time. The cosmological horizon of the universe was about $10^{-35}$ m. These are conditions so extreme that they cannot be recreated even in the most powerful particle accelerator in the world, the LHC at CERN in Geneva. To do this, according to Chasher and Nussinov's estimates, an enormous accelerator from about 30 parsecs (23 times the distance to the closest star, alpha Centaury) to 30 kiloparsecs (the size of the Galaxy) would be needed. In Planck's time, gravity, which in our world is enormously less intense than other forces, had an intensity comparable to other forces. We need a theory that brings together quantum mechanics and General Relativity, *quantum gravity*, which has not yet been formulated. In short, we cannot penetrate the secrets of the period from the Big Bang to the Planck era simply because we do not know the physics of that era. With the theories known today, we can try to describe what happened in the Universe only after Planck's time and from this epoch up to times of the order of $10^{-12}$ s our knowledge is based on theoretical ideas that have never been verified.

So let's start our story from the *Planck era*.

Due to the finiteness of the speed of light, an observer in the Planck epoch could not see farther than $10^{-35}$ m, a factor of $10^{20}$ smaller than the size of a proton. The Universe is dominated by the *quantum vacuum* from which particle-antiparticle pairs are created which, after infinitesimal times, annihilate and return to the vacuum. In the Planck era, all forces were unified. Just after the Planck era we have the *Era*

---

[1] In this book, temperatures are measured in degrees Kelvin, K. K is a unit of temperature measurement called Kelvin, in honor of William Thomson known as Lord Kelvin. To obtain the temperatures in degrees Centigrade, °C, just subtract 273.15 from the value in Kelvin.

| INTERLUDE 2 |
| :---: |
| **PARTICLES AND INTERACTIONS** |

The standard model contains two large families of particles: fermions and bosons. Fermions take their name from Enrico Fermi. They have semi-integer spin ($1/2$ $\hbar$, $3/2$ $\hbar$, $5/2$ $\hbar$…) and are the constituents of matter. Bosons take their name from Satyendranath Bose, follow the Bose-Einstein statistic and have integer spin ($0$ $\hbar$, $1$ $\hbar$, $2$ $\hbar$…), they are the mediators of forces. The spin is interpreted in a simplified way, even if incorrect, as a rotation around the axis of the system.

| **FERMIONS** |
| :---: |

*Hadrons* (from the Greek "strong"), are particles subject to the strong nuclear force and can be divided into

- *Barions* (from the Greek "heavy"): they are fermions. They are made up of nuclear particles, baryons, such as protons, neutrons, the $\Lambda$, Sigma, $\Delta$, $\Xi$, $\Omega$ particle and their respective antiparticles and heavier and non-nuclear particles, hyperons. Baryons are not elementary particles, but made up of quarks. There are six types of quarks: *up* (u), *down* (d), *strange* (s), *charm* (c), *bottom* (b) (or *beauty*), and *top* (t) (or *truth*). Quarks are combined into three pairs: (u, d), (c, s), (t, b), of increasing mass, and each with the same pair of charges $2/3$ e⁻, $-1/3$ e⁻. Each quark has three colors, so we have 18 quarks. Protons are made up of two up (up) and one down (down) quarks: (uud). Neutrons from one up and two down quarks (udd). Protons have a mass of about 938 MeV and neutrons are slightly more massive, 939 MeV and have a size of the order of $10^{-15}$ m. Outside the nucleus, neutrons are unstable and have an average lifespan of about 15 minutes. Protons are almost immortal particles, given that their average life is over $10^{34}$ years, much greater than the age of the universe. The average life of the proton is important because some Grand Unification Theories (GUT), theories that unify the strong, weak and electromagnetic nuclear forces, predict that the proton decays. The baryons are assigned the so-called *baryon number* which is $B = +1$ for baryons, $B = -1$ for antibaryons. For other particles, mesons and fermions $B = 0$. The baryon number is almost always a conserved quantity, i.e. the baryon number before a reaction is the same as the one after it.
- *Mesons* (from the Greek "middle"), are bosons subject to the strong nuclear force with intermediate masses between baryons and leptons. They consist of a quark and an antiquark.
- *Leptons* (from the Greek "light"), do not have a strong interaction, are elementary particles, and are fermions with spin $1/2$. Examples of this family are charged particles such as *electrons* with mass of about $10^{-30}$ kg (0.511 MeV) and dimensions less than $10^{-22}$ m, *muons* with mass 207 times that of the electron, *tau particles* with mass about 3500 times greater. than that of electrons, and their respective antiparticles or neutrinos like *neutrinos*. Neutrinos have a very small mass, between 10,000 or 1 million times smaller than that of the electron. They

*(Continued)*

*(Continued)*

| INTERLUDE 2 |
|---|
| **FERMIONS** |

come in 3 flavors: *electronic, muon and tau neutrino* and can oscillate, that is, transform into each other (neutrino oscillations). Like quarks, quark leptons have three generations of particles (e, $v_e$), ($\mu$, $v_\mu$), ($\tau$, $v_\tau$). Like baryons, leptons are assigned a lepton number, L = +1 for particles and L = −1 for antiparticles and L = 0 for hadrons.

Ultimately, we have three families of leptons, 6 particles, and three of baryons, another 6 particles. Each of the particles corresponds to an anti-particle of equal mass and opposite charge. A very interesting point is the fact that matter is made up of fermions and only particles of the first family, i.e., quarks u, d, electrons

| **BOSONS AND INTERACTIONS** |
|---|

There are four interactions or forces in nature: gravitational, *electromagnetic, strong nuclear and weak nuclear*.

The standard model only describes the last three.

- *Electromagnetic interaction*: interaction between charged particles and responsible for the electromagnetic field and electromagnetic waves. It can be attractive and repulsive. The electromagnetic force is mediated by the photon.
- *Strong nuclear interaction*: Responsible for the interaction between the quarks of the same protome or neutron (strong nuclear force) or on a larger scale between quarks of different protons and neutrons (strong residual force). In the first case the mediating particles are the gluons, in the second the pions. It has a range of action of the order of the size of the proton and grows as the distance decreases. It is treated internally by the theory called quantum chromodynamics.
- *Weak nuclear interaction*: responsible for the radioactive decay of atoms. It acts between leptons and quarks, between only leptons and between only quarks. It is mediated by the $W^+$, $W^-$, $Z^0$ bosons, vector bosons with mass about 90 and 100 times that of the proton, respectively. The weak nuclear force and electromagnetism are manifestations of a single force, the electroweak force.
- *Gravitational interaction*: responsible for the attractive interaction between massive objects. Not contemplated in the standard model. It is the weakest of the fundamental forces. It is mediated by the graviton.

*of the Grand Unification* which unfolds between $10^{-43}$ s and $10^{-36}$ s. At the beginning of this era, the force of gravity separates itself from the other forces, the electroweak one and the strong nuclear force which constitute a *superforce*. We are in the realm of the *Grand Unification Theory* (GUT). The temperature of the Universe decreases with expansion, and in this phase of the Universe the decrease was very rapid. Between the Planck era and the end of the *Grand Unification Era*, the temperature decreases to temperatures below $10^{30}$ K. At the end of this era, when the temperature reaches $10^{28}$ K, the Universe is subject to decoupling of the strong interaction from the electroweak force, which will constitute two separate forces. This phase is called the *grand unification phase transition*. Some types of *phase transitions* are present in everyday life. For example, the cooled water vapor turns into water at 100°C, and by further decreasing the temperature to 0°C the water turns into ice. In these transformations, heat, called *latent heat,* is released. Furthermore, we move from systems with higher symmetry to lower symmetry. For example, water is the same from any direction we look at it, it has greater symmetry, while ice has a crystalline structure and is not symmetrical like water. Due to the phase transition, an enormous amount of energy is released in the Universe, similar to what happens in the water-ice phase transition, which releases, as mentioned, latent heat. The Universe, of sub-nuclear dimensions, undergoes a metamorphosis, thanks to a period of exponential expansion, dubbed *inflation*, which develops in the period between $10^{-36}$ and $10^{-32}$ s. Remember that as we will see in Section 5.1 there is no overwhelming evidence for the existence of inflation.

From dimensions of the order of $10^{-28}$ m, the Universe grows by a factor of $10^{25}$–$10^{30}$, or perhaps higher. In an infinitely short time, the Universe reaches the size of a soccer ball. This huge expansion produces a drop in temperature. The universe is super cooled from $10^{27}$ to $10^{22}$ K and then heated again in the *reheating phase*. The release of the vacuum energy transforms the *virtual particles* that appeared and disappeared at the time of Planck into real particles. The universe is filled with radiation and elementary particles: quarks, leptons and their respective antiparticles (see Interlude 2 for a classification of particles). Inflation is a very important phase in the evolution of the universe. Although this phase is not yet well known, as demonstrated by the fact that there is not only one inflationary theory but several, it allows us to explain many things otherwise difficult to explain. Inflation solves a number of problems of the Big Bang cosmology. Explains the homogeneity of space, predicts that the universe is flat in accordance with the observations of the *cosmic microwave background*[2] (CMB), of which we will speak in more detail later. It foresees the generation of small inhomogeneities from which galaxies were formed. Finally, it predicts the existence of a background of primordial *gravitational waves*,[3] that is, waves produced by the motion of massive bodies (even if not charged). Finally, in the new versions of inflation, such as Linde's, inflation not only creates our universe, but creates infinite ones, the so-called *multiverse*.

Although there is a large group of physicists who study inflation, prominent physicists criticize it. Among them also Paul Steinhardt, who was one of its founders. As we will see in Section 5.1 he constructed an alternate model of the universe, called the *ecpirotic universe*, and an evolution of this, the *phoenix universe*.

These events occur between the GUT era, and an "extremely" long era, known as the *electroweak era,* that develops in the period between $10^{-36}$ and $10^{-12}$ s. In this era, the universe is full of particles and antiparticles that begin to collide and then annihilate leaving a surplus of matter particles that will then form our world.

At that time, the energies were so high that two photons colliding formed particles of matter which met with antimatter particles, annihilating each other. In short, there was a

---

[2] The cosmic background radiation, as already mentioned, is a sort of residual microwave sea that pervades the universe and reaches the Earth from all over the sky.

[3] The phenomenon is similar to what happens to any accelerated body. If the protons and electrons in an atom were not subject to the laws of quantum mechanics, due to the centripetal acceleration the electron would emit electromagnetic waves and precipitate on the proton in an infinitesimal time. As a charged body emits electromagnetic waves, similarly a massive one emits gravitational waves. Planned by Einstein in 1916, they were searched for decades and only discovered in 2015 thanks to the Ligo/Virgo collaboration. The first event revealed was that of two black holes one billion and three hundred million light years apart which in a slow dance and then more and more whirling up to reach speeds close to those of light, merged, generating a single black hole.

continuous flow of creation and destruction. At the end of the electroweak era, the weak nuclear force becomes a short-range force and separates into electromagnetic force and weak force. The Universe undergoes another phase transition. This transition is referred to as the *electroweak phase transition* or *spontaneous electroweak symmetry breaking.*

In the first billionth of a second ($10^{-12}$ s), the universe is made up of a plasma of quarks, leptons and gluons, Universe dimensions were approximately equal to the Earth-Sun distance. This quark soup called *quark-gluon plasma* was first observed at Brookhaven National Laboratory in 2002. As time goes by, the energy of quarks decreases and around $10^{-6}$ s, when the temperature drops below one thousand billion degrees, the universe is no longer able to keep separate the quarks that are companions to form the hadrons, which are a large family containing *baryons* (e.g., *protons, neutrons*) containing an odd number of quarks and mesons particles consisting of two quarks (cf. Interlude 2). Protons are almost eternal particles, while neutrons decay in 15 minutes. Meanwhile, the temperature continues to drop inexorably. The era just described is called the *quark era*. It extends between one billionth and one millionth of a second ($10^{-12}$–$10^{-6}$ s). Particles and antiparticles convert into photons, but photons are no longer energetic enough to create particle-antiparticle pairs. The universe is dominated by photons, electrons, neutrinos and a minority (one part in a hundred million) of protons and neutrons. When the temperature dropped below $10^{12}$ K this era, called *hadronic era* ($10^{-6}$–1 s), consisting of the confinement of quarks to form hadrons, ended. We arrive at the *lepton era* (1 s–3 minutes) dominated by leptons and antileptons. Electrons and positrons collide and annihilate each other generating photons which in turn collide forming other electron-positron pairs. The decrease in temperature and density produces a decrease in the reaction rate with the consequent decoupling of neutrinos when the universe was 1 second.

Returning to our history, the annihilation of most electrons has great effects on that of neutrons. In fact, in the *hadronic era*, neutrons do not disappear because they are formed by the fusion of protons and electrons with the production of neutrinos. Following the annihilation of electrons, protons can no longer generate neutrons whose number decreases. When the Universe is a little older than 1 second for every 10 protons there are only 2 neutrons. Neutrons are a little heavier than protons and decay in about 15 minutes. When the temperature was about $10^{10}$ K the neutrons were no longer created and the neutron-proton ratio was frozen, as already mentioned, at about 1 neutron for every 10 protons. Due to the decay of the neutrons their number, at 300 seconds when the temperature had dropped to about $10^9$ K, was reduced to 2 against a number of 14 protons. The number of neutrons and protons was sufficient to form 1 helium-4 nucleus leaving 12 protons. Since a helium nucleus is four times heavier than a hydrogen one, the fraction of helium-4 had to be given by 4 divided by 12 + 4 (16), and therefore in the universe there were about 25% helium and the 75% hydrogen. More in detail, when the temperature drops below a few billion degrees, protons and neutrons originate stable nuclei such as deuterium, which does not have a long life. Things change when the universe is about 3 minutes old. Deuterium no longer decays and helium-4, helium-3, lithium-7 are formed. We are in the *era of nucleosynthesis*, between 3 s and 20 minutes. As seen, the abundance of hydrogen (75%) and helium (25%) formed in nucleosynthesis depend on the density of protons and neutrons and of the radiation. These numbers were confirmed by the measurement of the abundance of the elements formed and have remained unchanged to this day, despite the transformation of hydrogen into helium in the stars. After about 20 minutes the temperature drops to the point where nuclear fusion stops.

The first calculations of nucleosynthesis were made in the '40s of the last century (1948) by Ralph Alpher and George Gamow, and published in the famous article αβγ, with the initials of Alpher, Bethe and Gamow. Primordial nucleosynthesis produces only light elements, up to beryllium. Since there is no stable nucleus with 8 nucleons, nucleosynthesis stops. Another fundamental prediction by Gamow, along with Alpher and Herman was that the universe should be immersed in a labile microwave radiation background, the famous CMB, with a temperature of 5 K.

Although this is not very well known, in 1950 Alpher and Herman managed to improve this estimate, obtaining the value 2.8 K, a value very close to the currently known value (2.725 K). This prediction was forgotten until the 1960s, when Penzias and Wilson accidentally discovered CMB.

At the turn of the *era of nucleosynthesis*, between 3 minutes and 240,000 years, we have the *era of radiation*. The universe contains plasma, an incandescent and opaque soup of protons and electrons. After the annihilation of leptons and anti-leptons, the energy of the universe is dominated by photons that interact with protons and electrons. Due to these continuous reactions, the light undergoes continuous deflections and reflections and is therefore trapped in the plasma. The universe is opaque and undetectable. The situation of the universe was very similar to that of when we find ourselves immersed in a very thick cloud or fog. Fog is a cloud that forms in contact with the ground and is made up of droplets of water and ice. If we are in the car, the light from the headlights cannot move freely because a photon in its motion will collide with the drops of water and will be reflected towards another drop and so on, remaining trapped. If the number of droplets decreases the photons will be freer to move and when the fog disappears, they will be able to move freely. This is what happens in the next phase, between 240000–380000 years called the *Age of Recombination/ Decoupling*. In the period ranging from about 260000 years to 380000 years (temperature 3000 K) the protons captured the electrons forming neutral atoms. The phenomenon is known as *recombination* (of electrons and nuclei), associated with the decoupling between radiation and matter. As the free electrons have decreased, the photons trapped by the interactions with the electrons and the photons become free to move and reach us and the *"fog"* that enveloped the universe disappeared and it became transparent and a cosmic background of visible light was released. This fossil fund, due to the expansion of the universe, is now observable in microwaves and is precisely the CMB.

After the formation of atoms practically nothing more happened, for hundreds of thousands of years, apart from the fact that the Universe continued to expand and consequently to cool.

## 2.2 The Cosmic Background Radiation

When the universe expands it cools, and the expansion "stretches" the wavelengths by increasing their length and decreasing the energy. The temperature decreases inversely proportional to the size of the universe, and the wavelength of photons grows with the size of the universe. Since energy is inversely proportional to the wavelength, photons will see their energy halve as the universe doubles in size.

The expansion from the time of recombination to now has made the universe enlarge by about a factor of one thousand, similar to the wavelengths. So, the photons of the background radiation are today a thousand times less energetic than at recombination. Similarly, the temperature from 3000 K has been reduced by a factor of 1000, and today it has temperatures of 2.725 K and a wavelength of 7.35 cm and is observed in the microwave spectral region. As already mentioned, this radiation which has the same temperature in all directions of the sky is indicated as already said with *Cosmic Microwave Background Radiation* or *CMB* (from Cosmic Microwave Background) and is considered as the fossil residue of the radiation emitted at the time of recombination and the Big Bang itself. This radiation was observed by chance in 1965 by two engineers Arno Penzias and Robert Wilson who were using a Bell telephone antenna to pick up signals from the Echo-1 and Telstar satellites. They discovered microwave radiation that did not change with the time of day or with the orientation. Not having a preferential direction, it was not possible that the radiation came from nearby New York, or from the Sun. Initially they thought it was produced by some interference or by the "white dielectric material", i.e., excrement, of a pair of pigeons, as Penzias called it, which housed in the antenna funnel. They consulted an MIT astronomer, Bernie Burke who knew about the studies of Robert Dicke and Jim Peebles of Princeton University. The scientists were planning an experiment to measure the background radiation, but they were preceded by the unsuspecting engineers. Penzias and Wilson published a short article in the Astrophysical Journal about what they had observed and in 1978 they won the Nobel Prize. In the previous pages of the same issue of the magazine, Dicke, Peebles and collaborators explained the origin of the signal.

The discovery, together with the expansion of the universe, and the abundance of light elements in the cosmos, was another confirmation and completion of the Big Bang theory. The radiation was proof that the universe had had a hot phase, confirming the ideas of de Sitter, Lemaitre, Gamow and other scientists.

A completely homogeneous and isotropic radiation, however, would have implied the impossibility of the formation of cosmic structures and therefore also of life. For this reason, it began to be suspected that there might be inhomogeneities that were observed in 1992 by the COBE satellite in an experiment conducted by George Smooth and John Mather who won the Nobel Prize in 2006 for the discovery. The observations showed that the background radiation is isotropic up to to 1 part in 100,000.

In 1990, Mather using COBE had also found that the radiation had the emission of a perfect black body,[4] i.e., an ideal object that absorbs all the incident radiation without reflecting it, with a temperature of 2.725 K. The observation confirmed Richard Tolman's prediction that in 1934 he had shown that black body radiation in an expanding universe cools but retains the same shape (continues to be described by a black body distribution at different temperatures). So, the

---

[4] A black body is an ideal object that absorbs all the incident radiation.

spectrum shape of the CMB, dating back two months after the Big Bang, has remained unchanged to this day.

Given the great importance of the CMB, experiments were carried out to measure its characteristics with an increasing degree of precision. This was done with successive experiments on balloons, such as BOOMERANG, or satellites such as WMAP and PLANCK, which allowed an increasingly in-depth study of the inhomogeneities of the background radiation, due to temperature differences and *density fluctuations*. Starting in 1997, three flights of a high-altitude balloon were carried out, the BOOMERANG experiment (acronym for Balloon Observations Of Millimetric Extragalactic Radiation and Geophysics). In 1997, the balloon flew in the skies of North America and in 1998 and 2003 in the skies of Antarctica. Like a real boomerang, exploiting the polar vortex, the balloon departed from the McMurdo base, flew at an altitude of 42 km to reduce the absorption of the CMB microwaves by the earth's atmosphere, and with a closed orbit returned to the point of departure. The experiment directed by Paolo De Bernardis and Andrew Lange provided a high-resolution image of the CMB anisotropies in a portion of the sky. Given the success of the experiment, NASA designed a space mission, WMAP (Wilkinson Microwave Anisotropy Probe) launched in 2001, followed by the PLANCK mission of the European Space Agency, launched in 2009.

The satellites produced a background radiation map consisting of warmer than average, colder areas, highlighting the temperature distribution of the plasma of which the universe was made up at 380,000 years after the Big Bang (Figure 2.1).

The map represents the small variations in temperature coming from the surface where photons last interacted with an electron, the so-called the *last scattering surface*, a sphere of the early universe at the center of which we are, or rather the surface of the cloud from which the light was diffused for the last time.

The fluctuations are isotropic up to 1 part in 100,000 and are visible in the map because they are greatly amplified. The hottest areas in the map correspond to the densest regions,

Figure 2.1.   Map of the CMB anisotropies obtained by the PLANCK mission: Source: ESA and PLANCK collaboration.

so the map also represents the density fluctuations in the early universe and could be defined as a snapshot of the universe at the time of recombination. The scales and magnitudes of these fluctuations determine what our current universe is. The fluctuations are loaded with information on the early universe.

## 2.3 The Dark Ages of the Universe

After recombination, the universe was made up of hydrogen, helium, and small amounts of deuterium formed during the *era of nucleosynthesis*, and hydrogen molecules ($H_2$). The photons of the CMB due to the expansion of the universe lost energy and the wavelengths were moved up to infrared, causing the universe to be deprived of visible light. Since there were no sources of light, such as stars, the universe was transparent, but dark.

This period is called the *dark age*, and it developed in the period between 380,000 years and the formation of the first stars, that is, a few hundred million years after the Big Bang. The only source of photons were hydrogen atoms that emitted radio waves of 21 cm, the so-called *HI* line, first observed in 1951 by Harold Ewen and Edward Purcell. This line is of fundamental importance for mapping neutral hydrogen in space.

These photons could theoretically be observed by radio telescopes, but so far this has not happened. Their revelation would allow to clarify various things, such as: the way in which matter was distributed in the dark age, how primordial stars were formed, and what was the role of recombination in the formation of galaxies.

The duration of this era is not known exactly, because it is not known with certainty when the first stars were formed. How do you estimate the epoch at which the reionization generated by the first stars began when the first stars were formed? The *Gunn-Peterson effect* is used.

In 1965, James Gunn and Bruce Peterson proposed that quasars, distant, very old, and very bright galaxies, could be used to date the final stages of reionization. According to the two researchers, neutral hydrogen produced a significant depression in the spectrum of high redshift quasars, at wavelengths shorter than 121.6 nanometers,[5] an effect confirmed in 2001 by a group of scientists led by Robert Becker. So, the dark age began after recombination, 380,000 years after the Big Bang, and ended about 300 million years after the Big Bang, when the first stars and galaxies were formed, which reionized the universe causing it to plunge back into darkness again, until about a billion years after the Big Bang.

## 2.4 The First Stars Appear

In the dark age the universe was dark until it was illuminated by the first stars.

These stars, not yet observed, were different from the present ones. In the first place they were much larger than today's stars: a few hundred times larger than the Sun. The mechanism that produced the energy was, as in today's stars, nuclear fusion, and in particular the dominant mechanism in the Sun: the *proton-proton chain*, in which four hydrogen nuclei are transformed into one of helium.

In stars more massive than the Sun, there is another type of process in which four protons again form a helium atom, with the help of carbon, nitrogen and oxygen. Due to the

---

[5] A nanometer is equal to one billionth of a meter.

absence of heavy elements such as carbon, the carbon cycle could not function in primordial stars. Moreover, if the first stars had worked with this mechanism, the nuclear processes would have been very fast and their life would have been very short. With the proton-proton chain their life is a little longer, about 10 million years, in any case a very short life compared to the life of a star like the Sun which lives about 10 billion years.

Furthermore, these stars, having formed from the gas that filled the universe, namely hydrogen and helium, were made up only of these elements. During their lifetime they produced elements heavier than hydrogen and when they exploded as a *pair-instability supernovae*,[6] they scattered them into space. The daughters of these stars were formed from the remains of primordial stars and contained in addition to hydrogen and helium traces of heavier elements. The primordial stars, called *population III*, in a hundred million years released a considerable amount of ultraviolet (UV) radiation which ionized the gas. The universe became opaque again. The expansion of the universe diluted the density of the plasma, until the photons were once again free to move freely in the Universe. So, the Universe knew more than one "*fiat lux*": with the Big Bang, after the recombination and finally at the end of the reionization.

## 2.5 The First Structures

After the formation of stars, structures such as galaxies were formed. In the dark age that we are considering, as in the rest of cosmic history, the expanding universe contained a gas made up of light elements and dark matter much more abundant than gas. What happened to the gas in the universe and to dark matter? In the early universe there were denser areas. These areas are the seeds from which the structures in the universe were formed. Thanks to the concentration of

---

[6] They are Supernovae due to the production of electron-positron pairs.

mass, the force of gravity was able to overcome the expansion of the universe and the concentrations of dark matter could collapse to form the so-called *dark matter halos*. The first ones that formed had masses of about a million suns. Gravity helped them grow, aggregating matter from their surroundings, so much so that today the largest of these halos have masses of one million billion Suns ($10^{15}$ $M_\odot$). Therefore, the dark matter first formed dark structures, (*dark matter halos*), which from the gravitational point of view behaved like sort of wells into which the gas later fell back, giving rise to visible objects such as galaxies. Dark matter first formed its structures because it was not subject to the action of photons, which in the case of ordinary matter did not allow atoms to form until recombination. At that time, ordinary matter, in the form of gas, began to be attracted to the dark one and fell into the wells formed by the dark matter, illuminating them. Thus, the galaxies were born. Before the galaxies with strange shapes were born which by aggregation gave rise to spiral galaxies. The collision of spiral galaxies originated elliptical galaxies. The formation and evolution of galaxies can be seen well in the image, called the *Hubble Deep Field* (HDF), containing about 10,000 galaxies and obtained using 800 exposures, which allows us to look at the universe from today to 13 billion years ago. In 2012, another image of a portion of the HDF was released combining 10 years of photographs of the region obtained by the Hubble Space Telescope. This image called *Extremely Deep Field* (XDF), is the deepest image of the sky ever obtained, allowing us to go back in time for 13.2 billion years. The image shows the dramatic birth of violently growing galaxies through collisions and mergers. Indistinct, fuzzy red galaxies are observed, remnants of dramatic collisions between galaxies. Scattered across the image, tiny, faint galaxies are observed, more distant than the red ones, which are the seeds from which today's galaxies were born. The youngest galaxies in XDF are only 450 million years after the Big Bang.

Spiral galaxies are made up of young stars (millions of years old) and gas arranged on a disk with spiral arms, a spherical central area called *bulge* containing older stars (billions of years old). The size of the stellar distribution, in an average spiral, is of the order of tens of kpc. The average elliptical galaxies have little gas and are spheroidal in shape, with stellar masses of the order of $10^{12}$ solar masses, about ten times larger than spiral ones. There are also *dwarf spheroids* and *irregular galaxies* with undefined shapes. Galaxies tend to cluster. Our galaxy is located in the local group, having a size of 1–2 Mpc, consisting of 3 main galaxies: our Galaxy, Andromeda and the Triangle and about seventy dwarf galaxies. There are clusters of larger galaxies called *galaxy clusters* containing thousands of galaxies and having dimensions of about ten Mpc and $10^{14}$–$10^{15}$ solar masses.

Even on a larger scale we have *superclusters* with dimensions of about a hundred Mpc. There are also spherical regions with very few galaxies called *voids* having sizes of 10–100 Mpc. The *large-scale structure* of the universe is made up of *filaments* at the intersection points of which clusters are formed. The whole resembles a cosmic web. The large-scale structure of our Universe resembles that of a sponge.

## 2.6 Planets are Formed

Planetary formation is a kind of by-product of star formation. From huge clouds of gas, called *molecular clouds*, in gravitational collapse it generates suns and planets. Gravitational collapse is most manifested in the densest regions of a molecular cloud and by the growth of the stellar embryos which has a duration ranging from hundreds of thousands to millions of years. Larger stars form faster. In the collapse the cloud becomes smaller and rotates faster and faster, forming an accretion disk, while the central temperature rises until nuclear reactions are triggered: a new star is born. After the formation of the star, the disk begins to cool, allowing the formation of grains of dust and ice.

These begin to collide with each other, building increasingly large objects that, influenced by gravity, form agglomerations. Objects grow up to a size of a few kilometers which will then give rise to *planetesimals* by aggregation, the seeds from which planets will be formed by growth. Far from the position where the Earth will form, planetary nuclei of about ten Earth masses will capture the surrounding gas, swept away by the Sun, forming the gaseous planets (Jupiter, Saturn, Uranus, Neptune). In the innermost area, where the Earth is located today, the planetesimals will continue their work of aggregation until the formation of the rocky planets we know (Mercury, Venus, Earth, Mars). Because of the collisions, the planets are glowing. The heavier materials (nickel, iron, etc.) sink towards the center, while the less light rocks will remain at the top. The metallic material that descends to the bottom, together with the Earth's rotation gives rise to the magnetic field, fundamental for life on Earth. Cosmic radiation destroys the chemical bonds of complex structures, and the magnetic field protects the Earth from this radiation. The Earth has its own atmosphere consisting of approximately 78% nitrogen, 21% oxygen, 0.9% argon and 0.04% carbon dioxide. Originally the atmosphere was very different, probably consisting of the gases that formed the nebula that originated the solar system: hydrogen, water vapor, methane, ammonia. Since then, volcanic activity, solar radiation, oxidative processes together with the activity of microbes and photosynthesis have significantly changed it. Even the collision of the Earth with an object similar to Mars caused changes due to the evaporation of the terrestrial rocks and the planet. The collision with the said planet threw a large part of the mass of the Earth into space which formed a disk and therefore led to the formation of the Moon. The latter is another witness to the great fortune under which the Earth was born. In fact, the Moon acts as a stabilizer of the Earth's axis, stabilizing the temperature, allowing the formation of climatic zones, and regular seasons. Another aspect that shows under what good auspices the Earth was born is the presence of giant planets, in particular Jupiter. With its enormous mass, more than three hundred times that of the Earth, Jupiter acts as a protective shield for the inner planets, defending them from impacts with comets and objects in general, that could create big problems for life, as happened for example sixty-five million years ago when the dinosaurs and various other living species died as a result of the impact of a meteorite about ten kilometers long. This was just one of many *mass extinctions* in Earth's history. Of course, life on Earth would not have been possible without the presence of liquid water. The Earth is not the only planet or satellite in the solar system on which there is water. Titan, the great satellite of Saturn has more water than the Earth, Europa, Jupiter's satellite has an underground ocean. On Mars, beyond the polar ice caps, water is present on the slopes of the planet. Enceladus, Saturn's satellite, should have an ocean of liquid water.

A unique feature of the Earth is the existence of a biosphere, not present in any of the terrestrial and extrasolar planets known to us. The birth of life on Earth is a discussed and unclear process.

## 2.7  Brief History of the Earth and Life

Earth formed about 4.54 billion years ago. In the first 600 million years (*Hadean aeon*) Earth continued to grow by accretion as the temperature increased. The heavier, more molten metal elements moved towards the center, thus forming the mantle and core. The atmosphere was made up of light elements, coming from the solar nebula, such as hydrogen and helium. The impact with a body the size of Mars, called *Theia*, threw part of the constituent material of the Earth into space, which over time formed the Moon. After the Hadean aeon we have the *Archean aeon* which is a long period ranging from 4 billion to 2.5 billion years ago. In this period the Earth was subject to intense volcanic phenomena and meteoric bombardment. The loss of the atmosphere after the impact with Theia caused the Earth to cool rapidly, forming a basalt crust. During the first Archean (3 billion years ago) the mantle temperature was probably 1600°C higher than today and gaseous vapors exhaled from the surface in addition to those coming from volcanoes. The fall of frozen asteroids, protoplanets and comets brought to Earth a significant amount of water, carbon dioxide, methane, ammonia, nitrogen, etc. The cooling of the planet produced the formation of clouds and the arrival of rains that gave rise to the oceans, about 4.2 billion years ago. The first components of the continental crust appeared in the Archean (4 billion years ago). The remains of these primordial continents are called *cratons* and are the nuclei around which the present continents were formed. Life began to form very early on primordial Earth.

There are two theories. The first theory, *panspermia*, assumes that life came from outside (for example on comets) and developed on Earth. In the second, life was born on Earth, perhaps around 4 billion years ago. Due to the formation and disappearance of the oceans, life probably formed more than once. Volcanic activity, lightning and ultraviolet radiation produced amino acids[7] from methane and ammonia, and over time much more complex molecules were formed. Moving forward, a *replicator* emerged, probably the *RNA* (ribonucleic acid), which was then replaced by *DNA* (deoxyribonucleic acid) (see Chapter 10). The latter is a double helix macromolecule containing the genetic information for protein synthesis. RNA, similar to DNA but with a single helix, converts the genetic information of DNA into proteins. It is a molecule like a sort of dictionary of genetic information, which translates the coded language of DNA, that is, the nucleotide segments (genes), into the amino acids of proteins. We know that DNA is found in the nucleus of cells which are surrounded by a membrane. Then cell membranes were formed. The order of formation, first RNA and then membranes or vice versa, is debated as we will see in Chapter 10. It is thought that the first replicator was RNA since it contains both genetic information and catalyzes reactions. DNA replaced RNA, and enzymes (which are proteins) began to function as catalysts for reactions. RNA continued to play the role of transferring information and synthesizing proteins. The next aeon is

---

[7] They are the primary structural unit of proteins. They can be thought of as building blocks that form a long sequence that gives rise to a protein.

called *Proterozoic* (2.5 billion–542 million years ago). It was in this period that the present continents were formed from the cratons. The development of the atmosphere and the appearance of oxygen upset the equilibrium that had been created and from *prokaryotes*[8] it passed to *eukaryotes*. During the Proterozoic there were important glaciations and the Earth turned into a sort of snowball. Probably the first cells were *heterotrophic*, that is, they used the surrounding organic molecules as a source of energy and raw material. Slowly they began to use sunlight as an energy source with a system similar to photosynthesis. *Autotrophic* cells also appeared, capable of synthesizing their own organic molecules from inorganic substances and from sunlight or in other forms. The life forms that developed are classified into three domains: the *bacteria* that were probably the first to separate from other life forms, the *archaea* (or ancient bacteria), and the *eukaryotes*. Archaea, bacteria and eukaryotes continued to differentiate and become increasingly sophisticated. About 900 million years ago, the first multicellular beings were formed. In the aeon following the *Paleozoic* (542–252 million years) the amount of oxygen increased a lot due to photosynthesis and an ozone layer was formed that allowed the single-celled organisms that reached the emerged earth to survive. The first vertebrates, ancestors of modern fish, were formed at the beginning of this aeon, about 530 million years ago. The first plants and fungi began to grow at the edges of the aquatic environment and to move on land and the animals behaved similarly. The oldest fossils of fungi and plants date back to 480 million years ago and the arthropods which are invertebrates such as crustaceans, insects etc., moved on earth 450 million years ago followed by the *tetrapods* (vertebrates with four limbs) which developed from fish and from them *amphibians* were born. About 310 million years ago the *synapsids* (including mammals) separated from the *sauropsids* (including birds and reptiles). The Earth was

---

[8] Prokaryotes represent one of the domains in which living organisms are divided: Archaea and Bacteria. They are characterized by the absence of a nucleus and a membrane system typical of eukaryotes.

dominated for a period of more than 150 million years (from 230 million to 65 million years ago) by the dinosaurs who disappeared due to the collision of a meteorite ten kilometers long that fell off the Yucatan peninsula. Mammals already inhabited the Earth and until recently it was believed they were small in size. However, a huge dicynodon was discovered in Poland a few years ago, a herbivorous mammal as big as an elephant. To reach man, one has to wait many millions of years. The first differentiation of the primate branch that led to the development of man occurred 6 million years ago and probably two million years ago the first specimens of the genus *Homo* appeared. Of particular interest are the remains found in the Afar triangle by the palentologists Coppens, Taieb and Gray of a young female specimen of Astrolopitecus that lived about 3.2 million years ago and called *Lucy*. This species was most likely bipedal, but the skull was still ape-like. Although he was bipedal, he lived partly in trees. Several other finds of 13 individuals were made in 1975, dating back at least 3.2 million years and in 2000 a specimen was found a few kilometers from Lucy's location, a 3-year-old female named Selam, was found. Until a few years ago it was thought that *Homo sapiens* appeared probably 200,000 years ago in sub-Saharan Africa, but the findings at the Jebel Irhoud site in Morocco dating back to 350,000–300,000 years ago led to think that the whole of Africa was the cradle of modern civilization and that Homo sapiens appeared earlier than previously thought. The oldest finds in Europe are those of the Bacho Kiro cave in Bulgaria, dating back to 45 thousand years ago. It is thought that groups of Homo sapiens left Africa 60,000 years ago, then took over all other human species and progressively colonized the planet.

## Summary: Key Points

- The universe originated 13.8 billion years ago. Its initial state was very hot and dense and did not contain the objects and particles that make it up today.
- After an exponential expansion in the period $10^{-35}$–$10^{-32}$ s,

the microscopic region that made up the universe was transformed into a region the size of a soccer ball.
- The rapid decrease in temperature leads to the formation of hadrons around $10^{-6}$ s and nuclei formed 3 minutes after the Big Bang.
- It takes up to 380,000 years for electrons and protons to combine to form hydrogen atoms. In the recombination of electrons and protons, the cosmic background radiation was generated.
- After a few hundreds of millions of years, stars and later galaxies were formed.
- The Earth formed around 4.5 billion years ago and life appeared around 4 billion years ago

# CHAPTER 3

# WHY IS THERE SOMETHING OUT OF NOTHING? MATTER-ANTIMATTER ASYMMETRY

*"Nothing is more real than nothing."*

— Samuel Beckett

The world around us seems to be a *continuum*, that is, objects can be divided indefinitely. Anaxander, Anaximenes, Empedocles had built up a special idea of an *element* that was based on the idea of the continuum. Thanks to Aristotle these ideas rose to the rank of philosophy. He imagined that the world under the moon was composed of four elements: earth, water, air and fire, while the Sun and the stars were composed of a fifth element: the ether. This misconception dominated Western culture for millennia. *Atomist theory*, supported by Leucippus and Democritus and their followers, had a completely different point of view. According to this theory matter is made up of non-divisible basic elements, hence the term *atom*: indivisible, into more elementary elements. The cosmos was made up of an empty and unlimited space within which the atoms moved continuously, in a casual motion, which combined to give rise to material bodies. Only after two thousand years, the ideas of the atomists were proved to be correct. Dalton's *atomic hypothesis* led to the first atomic theory of matter. Several other scientists tried to order the elements into groups with similar characteristics. Dmitri Mendeleyev in 1869 proposed a *periodic system of elements* that showed the variation of the chemical-physical properties when the elements were ordered according to increasing values of the atomic number. However, in the twentieth century several scientists, such as Ernst Mach, considered it an abstruse question, with no possibility of being verified. In 1905, Einstein with the interpretation of

*Brownian motion*[1] indirectly showed the existence of atoms. Today the existence of atoms is no longer in doubt. They are characterized by different sizes depending on how many basic components (protons, neutrons, electrons) they contain. It took about a hundred years and a great deal of theoretical and experimental effort to arrive at the formulation of a complete theory describing the fundamental interactions and the particles associated with them, the so-called *standard model of particles* that describes all fundamental particles and interactions except gravity.

## 3.1 Fields and Interactions

As we mentioned, today we have a model capable of describing three of the four fundamental interactions and the elementary particles related to them: the standard model of particles. The model is basically a quantum field theory. What does it mean? What is a field? A field is a function that assigns a value to each point in space. To understand, each point of a room has a temperature and the set of all these temperatures is the temperature range of the room. This particular type of field is called a *scalar field* because it associates a number with each point of space, the temperature values (Fig. 3.1, left).

Similarly, on a windy day every point in space will correspond to the speed and direction of the wind. This is also a field, but a *vector field*, because at each point you need to know three quantities to define the field (Figure 3.1, right). However, these fields are not fundamental fields, they are properties of the air. The gravitational and electromagnetic fields, on the other hand, are fundamental fields. A field easy to visualize is the magnetic field. It is enough to do a well-known experiment, placing on a surface some iron filings and

---

[1] That is, the random motion of particles suspended in a fluid. These movements had been explained by Einstein assuming the existence of molecules in the fluid which, colliding with the suspended particles, caused their motion.

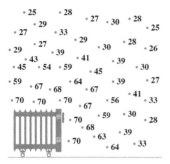
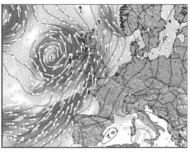

Figure 3.1.   Left: temperature field. A temperature is associated with each point. Right: Wind field in Europe. The yellow arrows indicate the direction and intensity of the wind (the larger the arrow, the stronger the wind). Source: Tide-forecast.com

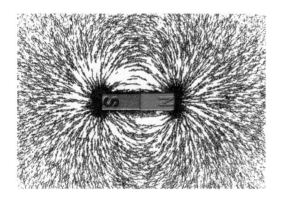

Figure 3.2.   magnetic field lines of a magnet.

under the surface a magnet. The magnetic field lines will then be clearly visible (Fig. 3.2).

Another fundamental field is the gravitational one. By applying quantum theory to fields, a *quantum field* is obtained, subject to the rules of quantum mechanics. Unlike classical fields, a quantum field does not associate a number to each point but a function, an infinite number of points. In the case of quantum fields, for example, if we measure the energy in a room, in the quantum field this will not be able to assume all the values it wants, but only multiple values of a fundamental quantity. Furthermore, we could not say that an energy is associated with a certain point in the field, but we can only indicate the probability that a certain energy value is associated with a point. In the view of modern physics, reality is made up of fields. The world is made up of fields, entities that permeate space and manifest themselves through their vibrations.

In this view, particles and antiparticles are not fragments of matter, but packets of energy, or rather vibrations of quantum fields. Looking at a field in detail, we see it "resolving" into particles. Like every daughter, each particle has its own father, a particular field. For example, the particles, called photons, are children of the electromagnetic field. The energy of one field can be transferred to another through interactions, a phenomenon present in the processes in which a set of initial particles are transformed into another set of final particles. Fields are the real building blocks of which matter is made and beyond that they make interactions possible, that is, the fundamental forces of nature. A very interesting thing is the fact that for quantum mechanics, in our world, the vacuum is not empty as we imagine it, but it is made up of fields.

## 3.2 Particles

If the fundamental building blocks that make up the world are the fields, their oscillations manifest themselves as particles. The standard model contains two large families of particles: fermions and bosons.

*Fermions* take their name from Enrico Fermi and obey the *Pauli exclusion principle.* They follow the *Fermi-Dirac statistic* and therefore have a half integer spin[2] (1/2 $\hbar$, 3/2 $\hbar$, 5/2 $\hbar$...)

---

[2] Spin was introduced in 1925 by Goudsmit and Uhlenbeck to explain previous experiments. They suggested that electron had an *intrinsic angular momentum,* that is, it was rotating around its own axis like a top. Often, in popular book this idea is used, even if not correct. Spin, as shown by Dirac, comes out automatically in the relativistic version of quantum mechanics. It is a quantum number that together with other quantum numbers describe

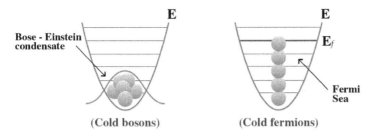

Figure 3.3. Bosons and fermions. Source: modification of work by Fred Bellaiche.

and are the constituents of matter. There are two types of fermions: the quarks constituting the protons and neutrons, and the leptons: electrons, muons, tau particles, neutrinos and their respective antiparticles.

The *bosons* take their name from Satyendranath Bose, they follow the *Bose-Einstein statistic* and from the *spin-statistic theorem,* they have integer spin (0 ħ, 1 ħ, 2 ħ…).

Fermions, following Pauli's exclusion principle, occupy much more space than bosons as shown in Fig. 3.3. On the left side is represented a gas of bosons and on the right one of fermions at temperatures close to absolute zero (−273.16°C). The boson gas collapses to form a *Bose-Einstein condensate.* Fermions cannot place themselves in a state that takes up little space. They arrange to occupy energetic states of increasing energy up to a state of maximum energy called *Fermi energy.* This is why fermions are the constituents of matter, while bosons are the vectors of interactions.

Bosons are distinguished in *gauge bosons* or vectors that mediate the forces and in *mesons*, stable particles consisting of a quark and its antiparticle, antiquark. Particles composed of a large number of particles, such as protons and neutrons, and atomic nuclei can behave like bosons or fermions depending on the total spin. Another classification of the particles

---

the quantum state of a particle. The value of the spin of a particle describes to which family the particle belongs, as we will see in the following.

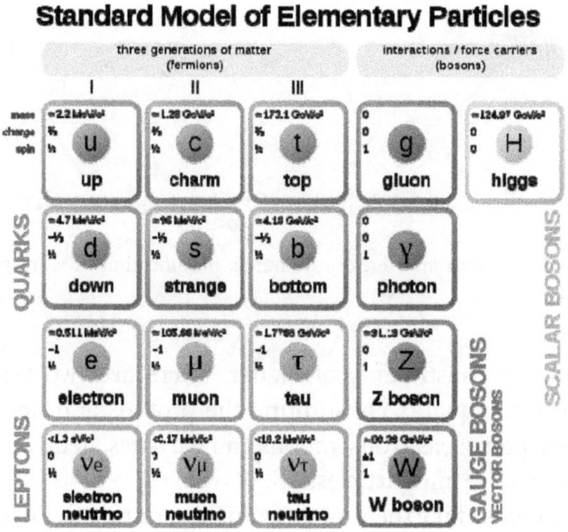

## Standard Model of Elementary Particles

Figure 3.4.    particles and interactions in the standard model.
Credit: Wikipedia

according to the interactions to which they are subjected or their mass is as follows:

1.  *Hadrons* (from the Greek "strong"), are particles subject to strong nuclear force and can be divided into
    *   *Barions* (from the Greek "heavy"): they are fermions. They consist of nuclear particles, the baryons, such as protons, neutrons, the particle $\Lambda$, *Sigma*, $\Delta$, $\Xi$, $\Omega$ (and their respective antiparticles) and heavier and non-nuclear particles, *hyperons*. Baryons are not elementary particles but made up of *quarks*. There are six types of quarks: *up (u), down (d), strange (s), charm (c), bottom (b) (or beauty), and top (t) (or truth)*. The quarks are combined in three pairs: (u, d), (c, s), (t, b), of increasing mass, and each with the same pair of charges 2/3 e⁻, –1/3 e⁻ (where e⁻ is the electron charge). Each quark has *three colors*, so we have 18 quarks. Protons consist of two up (u) and one down (d) quarks: (uud). Neutrons from one quark up

40

and two down (udd). Protons have a mass of about 938 MeV and neutrons are slightly more massive, 939 MeV and have a size of the order of $10^{-15}$ m. Outside the nucleus, neutrons are unstable and have an average life of approximately 15 minutes. Protons are almost immortal particles, given that their average life is greater than $10^{34}$ years, much greater than the age of the universe. The average life of the proton is important because some *Grand Unification Theories* (GUT), theories that unify the strong, weak and electromagnetic nuclear forces, require that the proton decays. The baryons are assigned the so-called *baryonic number* which is $B = +1$ for the baryons, $B = -1$ for the anti-baryons. For the other particles, mesons and fermions $B = 0$. The baryon number is an almost always preserved quantity, i.e., the baryon number before a reaction is the same as the one after.

- *Mesons* (from the Greek "middle"), are bosons subject to strong nuclear force with intermediate masses between the baryons and the leptons. They consist of a quark and an antiquark.
- *Leptons* (from the Greek "light"), have no strong interaction, are elementary particles, and are fermions with spin 1/2. Examples of this family are charged particles such as electrons having a mass of about $10^{-30}$ kg (0.511 MeV) and dimensions less than $10^{-22}$ m, *muons* with a mass 207 times that of the electron, *tau* particles with a mass about 3500 times larger than that of electrons, and their respective antiparticles. The family also contains neutral particles, the *neutrinos*. Neutrinos have a very small mass, between 10,000 or 1 million times smaller than that of the electron. They come in 3 flavors: *electronic neutrino, muonic* and *tauonic* and can oscillate, that is, transform into each other (*neutrino oscillations*). Like quarks, leptons have three generations of particles $(e, v_e), (\mu, v_\mu), (\tau, v_\tau)$. Like baryons, leptons are assigned a leptonic number, $L = + 1$ for particles and $L = -1$ for antiparticles and $L = 0$ for hadrons.

Ultimately, we have three families of leptons, 6 particles, and three of baryons, another 6 particles. To each of the particles corresponds an anti-particle of equal mass and opposite charge.

A very interesting point is that matter is made by fermions and only by particles of the first family, namely quarks u, d, and electrons. A legitimate question at this point is wondering why there are two other families of particles if they do not constitute matter and why there is a mass hierarchy. This and many other questions, show the limitations of the *standard model*.

## 3.3 Interactions

In nature there are four interactions or forces: *gravitational, electromagnetic, strong nuclear and weak nuclear interaction.*
The standard model only describes the last three.

- *Electromagnetic interaction*: it can be attractive and repulsive and decays with the square of the distance. It is responsible for electromagnetic phenomena (emission and absorption of radiation) and chemical reactions. It holds electrons around nuclei. The electromagnetic interaction is mediated by the *photon*, this means that the interaction is due to the photon.
- *Strong nuclear interaction*: it is the most intense. It is responsible for the existence of the atomic nucleus, has a range of action in the order of the size of the proton and grows as the distance decreases. It is mediated by 8 bosons, the *gluons*.
- *Weak nuclear interaction*: it is responsible for radioactive decay, contributes to making the stars shine. It has three mediators, the bosons $W^+$, $W^-$, $Z^0$, which unlike the mediators of the other interactions have mass, respectively 90 and 100 times heavier than the proton. Their mass comes directly from the Higgs mechanism. The weak and electromagnetic interactions are manifestations of a single interaction, the *electroweak interactions*.

- *Gravitational interaction*, although not described by the standard model, it is of fundamental importance. It has a never-observed theoretical mediator, the *graviton*. It is the weakest of interactions, $10^{25}$ times less intense than the weak one, $10^{36}$ than the electromagnetic one, $10^{38}$ than the strong one, but dominates in large spaces and in the universe. It is always attractive and responsible for the formation of structures, the rotation of planets around stars, galaxies and so on.

Before concluding we want to recall the *Higgs field* and the related particle the *Higgs boson*, discovered in 2012, which supplies mass to elementary particles such as quarks and $W^+$, $W–Z^0$ bosons. Its measured mass is 125 GeV.

The 12 elementary particles do not feel the various interactions in the same way. All "feels" the gravitational interaction, while only the charged ones perceive the electromagnetic interaction. Strong interaction is felt only by quarks.

Protons, neutrons and electrons form *atoms*. The simplest one, the hydrogen atom, is made from a proton and an electron. A gold atom has 79 protons and 118 neutrons, and for electrical neutrality, 79 electrons. An atom is basically an empty structure. To get an idea, if the core had the diameter of a tennis ball (7 cm in diameter), the closest electron would be at a distance of 3 km.

## 3.4 Matter Antimatter Asymmetry

As we have seen in Chapter 2, the Big Bang created an equal amount of matter and antimatter. The particles of matter and antimatter are created in pairs, they have the same mass but opposite charge and if they meet, they annihilate leaving only energy behind. However, today's universe seems to be predominantly made up of matter. Where did all the antimatter go? The origin of matter is one of the greatest mysteries of physics. Since the world is made of matter, it must be assumed that in some phase of the evolution of the

Universe an asymmetry has been created between matter and antimatter. With the use of an accelerator such as the LHC we are able to study the universe up to about $10^{-12}$ s when it was made up of a plasma of quarks and gluons. Before this moment we can only rely on our theories and extrapolate to energies that have never been experimentally tested. It was in this time interval that the excess of matter over antimatter was generated which gave rise to 4.9% of the energy mass of the Universe. The remaining 95.1% is made up of *dark matter*[3] and *dark energy.*[4]

One might think that antimatter is segregated in some regions of the Universe, but very large regions of the sky have shown no evidence of radiation from the border areas. Today there are two paths taken to explain matter-antimatter asymmetry, *electroweak baryogenesis*, now in crisis, and *baryogenesis via leptogenesis*, that is, the origin of baryons through that of leptons. In 1967, the Russian physicist Sakharov published the article *Violation of CP symmetry, C asymmetry and baryon asymmetry of the Universe* in which three conditions were introduced for the origin of matter-antimatter asymmetry. The first condition was the

1.  violation of symmetries C and CP.

The first symmetry, C, the charge conjugation changes a particle into an antiparticle, while the P symmetry, where P stands for "parity", is the operation that changes the sign of the spatial coordinates, providing a mirror image of the physical system.

The other condition is

2.  the non-conservation of the baryon number B, which is a necessary but not sufficient condition because C would

---

[3] Dark matter is a hypothetical form of matter thought to account for approximately 27% of the total matter in the universe. Various astrophysical observations imply dark matter's presence.

[4] Dark Energy is a hypothetical form of energy that exerts a negative, repulsive pressure, behaving like the opposite of gravity.

lead to opposite violations in the sign that would cancel any excess of the baryon number.

Finally,

3. the reactions must occur out of thermodynamic equilibrium.

One may wonder whether these conditions are met. In the 1950s, physicists Tsung Dao Lee and Chen Ning Yang proposed an experiment to verify the conservation of parity in the weak interaction. In the winter of 1956–1957, Madam Wu and collaborators studied the decay of cobalt-60 showing that the P symmetry was not preserved. In 1964, Kronin and Fitch showed in an experiment with neutral kaons, $K^0$, and its antiparticle, that the CP symmetry was not respected. More recently, the experiments *Babar* (in the Stanford Linear Accelerator Center in the USA) and *Belle* (in the High Accelerator Research Organization in Tsukuba, Japan) have shown the violation of the CP symmetry in several processes involving the so-called B mesons. As previously discussed, when the Universe was one billionth of a second old (energy greater than 246 GeV) the weak and electromagnetic interactions were unified in the electroweak interaction, the mediators were massless particles ($W_1$, $W_2$, $W_3$ and the photon, $\gamma$). One billionth of a second after the Big Bang the *electroweak phase transition* occurred, in which the electroweak force split into weak and electromagnetic interaction, the first mediated by the massive bosons $W^+$, $W^-$, $Z^0$, and the second by the photon. In 1985, Vadim Kuzmin, Valerij Rubakov, and Mikhail Shaposhnikov showed that there were configurations called sphalerons[5] that allowed the transition between states with different baryon numbers and were not suppressed by the increase in temperature.

More precisely, only groups of three baryons into three antileptons (or three antibaryons into three leptons) and vice versa can be converted, violating the conservation of

---

[5] A sphaleron is a time-independent solution of the electroweak field equations and involved in processes that violate the baryon and lepton number.

the baryon and lepton number. As one would expect, the breaking of the electroweak symmetry destroyed the thermal equilibrium of the sphaleronic processes, so that under the transition temperature the violation of the baryon number was no longer preserved. Therefore, we know that the CP symmetry is violated, the baryon number is not conserved due to the sphaleronic processes, so the third condition remains to be verified: the breakdown of the thermal equilibrium. An example of breaking the thermal equilibrium is that of a closed pot with a lid. The water molecules leave the liquid phase and pass to the vapor phase. When an equilibrium temperature is reached, the number of molecules that pass from the liquid to the gas phase is equal to those that carry out the reverse process. If you remove the lid, the balance is broken. A similar thing happens in the electroweak phase transition (if it is of first order[6]) in which bubbles of the electromagnetic phase are formed and expand into the electroweak one. The bubble walls create the thermodynamic imbalance to satisfy Sakharov's third condition. So, in the electroweak transition all the requirements requested by Sakharov[7] are verified.

In order for the sphaleronic processes to be able to produce the observed asymmetry, a certain intensity is required in the phase transition. This depends on the Higgs bosons and on a not

---

[6] First-order phase transitions are those that involve *latent heat*, such as that emitted by ice when it melts.

[7] More in detail, due to the CP violation, the bubble wall has a selective permeability to the passage of quarks and antiquarks. If the flow of quarks towards the inside of the bubble is favored, an excess of quarks will form inside the bubble and an excess of antiquark on the outside. Meanwhile, the bubbles expand until they occupy all the fluid. The external antiquarks should fall inside the bubbles and, meeting the quarks, cancel the asymmetry. However, this does not happen due to the sphaleronic processes. Outside the bubble, the antiquarks dominate, the processes that increase the number of quarks or reduce that of the antiquark dominate the inverse processes until equilibrium is re-established and the asymmetry is canceled. Inside the bubbles, the sphaleronic processes are much less intense than outside and therefore we find ourselves with an excess of quarks. When the bubbles have taken up all the space and the electroweak transition is complete, we will be left with an excess of quarks.

too high mass of the top quark. From the measurements of these two quantities, we know that the phase transition is too weak to explain the baryogenesis. To solve the problem, the use of new physics such as supersymmetry[8] (which we will discuss in Section 5.2) is invoked. However, even so the problem cannot be solved.

The other path that remains is that of *baryogenesis via leptogenesis*. This is based on the fact that the sphalerons involve the leptons as well as the baryons. Therefore, creating a lepton asymmetry produces a baryon asymmetry. A model used is that in which leptogenesis arises from the decay of massive neutrinos. Here too there is a problem: it is not clear whether leptogenesis can be verified directly.

Ultimately, to date no mechanism has been found that can explain the matter-antimatter asymmetry problem. This means that we are unable to answer the question *"why is there something rather than nothing"* with certainty.

## Summary: Keynotes

- It took millennia for the idea that the world is made of atoms to assert itself and about a century to arrive at the formulation of a theory of the particles that make up the Universe and of the fundamental interactions, the so-called *standard model of particles*.
- Before the standard model was developed several decades passed necessary for the development of quantum mechanics and quantum field theory.
- Material objects are made up of *fermions*, and the interactions are mediated by *bosons*.
- The mediator bosons of the strong interaction are 8 *gluons*, those of the electroweak force the bosons $W^+$, $W^-$, $Z^0$, and that of electromagnetism is the photon. The particles are 6 quarks organized into two families and then the leptons: the *electron*, the *muon*, the *tau particle* and the respective *neutrinos*.

---

[8] Supersymmetry is a theory that assumes that to each boson corresponds a fermion and vice versa.

- Elementary particles have mass thanks to the existence of the Higgs boson, and Higgs mechanism.
- One would expect that in the world there was the same amount of matter and antimatter, but in reality, there is an asymmetry in favor of matter. It is not yet clear what are the reasons that led to this asymmetry. However, asymmetry can be seen as one of those "coincidences" (or by converse as a part of a project) that allow the Universe to be as we see it and for life to exist.

# CHAPTER 4

# THE BANG OF THE BIG BANG

*"The Big Bang theory never was a theory of the bang. It said nothing about what banged, why it banged, or what happened before it banged".*

— Alan Guth

We know that the Universe began 13.8 billion years ago. The beginning is usually indicated by the term Big Bang and in the common imagination it was a great explosion. It is well known that the Big Bang was not this. For Jim Peebles, Nobel prize and one of the nowadays greatest cosmologists,

> the first thing to understand about my field is that its name, Big Bang Theory, is quite inappropriate.... It [the theory] connotes the notion of an event and a position, both of which are quite wrong

There is no evidence of a gigantic explosion that occurred at the origin of the times, again from Peebles' point of view. Among other things, the period that goes from instant zero to time $10^{-43}$ s, known as Planck's time, cannot be studied both for lack of observational data and for the lack of a theory that describes it. Moreover, from the ideas that come from cosmology up to times close to those of Planck, the Universe was much smaller than that of any elementary particle. The term Bang therefore seems not very adequate given that from time zero (Big Bang) to times of the order of $10^{-35}$ s there does not seem to have been a rapid expansion produced by an initial explosion. It seems more likely what Alan Guth claims

> *In its original form, the Big Bang theory never was a theory of the bang. It said nothing about what banged, why it banged, or what happened before it banged.*

For Guth, the bang of the Big Bang is what is referred to as the theory of inflation

> *I usually describe inflation as a theory of the "bang" of the Big Bang*

The theory or theories of inflation that we will discuss in this chapter describe how the Universe transformed from a tiny region into a region the size of a soccer ball in a tiny fraction of a second. Although many scientists believe in the theory, others detest it and apart from personal tastes, as we will see, inflation still has to pass several tests for it to become the theory that produced the "bang" of the Big Bang.

## 4.1 Guth Inflation

Just after the origin of the Universe around $10^{-35}$ s, the Universe underwent an exponential expansion that took it from microscopic to macroscopic dimensions, increasing its radius by a factor of $10^{25}$-$10^{30}$.

There are various models of inflation, but almost all agree in the hypothesis that inflation is driven by an unknown *scalar field* (similar to the Higgs field) called *inflaton*, and that there is a *spontaneous symmetry breaking.*

The first inflation theory was first proposed in 1979 by Alexei Starobinski and a few years later by Alan Guth. It was introduced to solve some of the problems of cosmology of the time, such as

- the *horizon problem*, that is the problem of explaining how regions of the Universe that are not causally connected, i.e., larger than the dimensions that light could cross, generating thermal equilibrium, have given rise to a homogeneous and isotropic universe as seen in CMB.

- the *problem of flatness*. If today the density of the Universe differed by less than 1% from the critical one, in the early Universe the deviation should be less than one part in $10^{61}$. The exponential expansion of the Universe has made the Universe flat. To give an illustrative example, it is very difficult for us terrestrial observers to realize that we live on a sphere, being the radius of our planet enormously greater than our size.
- the *problem of topological defects*, such as magnetic monopoles that should be present in the Universe but are not.

Guth's initial theory is based on a concept of quantum field physics, the *vacuum energy*.

In quantum mechanics, this entity does not correspond to the common notion of vacuum as the absence of everything, but to the minimum of energy of quantum fields.

The quantum vacuum is a sort of sea full of particles and antiparticles, dubbed *virtual particles*, which are born and annihilate rapidly and which ensure that the energy of the field cannot be completely null. This continuous birth and death and the fluctuations of the vacuum are governed by *Heisenberg's uncertainty principle*.

This principle requires that some physical quantities, called *conjugate variables*, such as energy and time or position and moment, i.e., mass times speed, are subject to a certain degree of uncertainty. In other words, in a physical system all the values of the physical observables cannot be determined simultaneously, unlike what happens in classical physics which can be described by all the values of the quantities observable in it, because they are all defined. According to *Heisenberg's uncertainty principle* (see section 6.1 for a broader description) the more accurately the position is measured the less is known of the moment and the tyranny of the uncertainty principle also applies to energy, $E$, and the time, $t$. The important thing to remember is that this principle does not depend on the accuracy of the experiments.

Even in an ideal and perfect experiment, uncertainty would continue to exist. So not only it is not possible to know the exact energy of a system in a certain instant, but if we wanted to determine exactly the energy of the system, we would need an infinite time. As a consequence, a system does not have an energy defined in every instant, but it changes, fluctuates, permanently, i.e., its value increases and decreases compared to what we would expect and all this at a speed that cannot be measured directly. In other words, the conservation of energy can be violated, but only for very short periods of time: the less is the energy present in the fluctuation, the longer it can persist. Quantum uncertainty allows small amounts of energy to appear from nowhere, always on the condition that they disappear in a very short time. This energy can take the form of very short-lived pairs of particles and antiparticles, called, as reported, *virtual particles*, such as an electron-positron pair. Therefore, the *Heisenberg uncertainty principle* causes the more uniform environment to necessarily present irregularities at the quantum level. According to Guth, the Universe was initially in a state of false vacuum. To explain what a false vacuum is, let's consider Fig. 4.1.

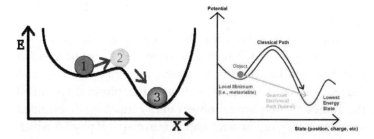

Figure 4.1.   Collapse of the false vacuum. State 1 is a local minimum of energy and constitutes the *false vacuum*. State 3 represents the lowest possible energy state and is the *true vacuum*. A transition from false vacuum to true vacuum is possible by means of a quantum mechanical effect called the tunnel effect. The transition from state 1 to state 3 constitutes the collapse of the false vacuum.
*Source*: Wikipedia

We represent the energetic state of the Universe with a ball. The Universe can be in state 1. This is a minimum of unstable energy. In the same figure we observe that there is another state, state 3, a minimum that has lower energy and is stable. State 1 is denoted by the term *false vacuum* because it is not the lowest energy minimum. Instead state 3 is the lowest theoretically conceivable level and is the *"true" vacuum*. So, for Guth our universe was initially in the state 3, a *false vacuum*. In quantum mechanics it can happen that the Universe transits from state 1 of false vacuum to 3 of true vacuum through a process called *tunnel effect*, as shown in Figure 4.1. Before moving on, it is better to clarify what *quantum tunneling* is. In classical mechanics, due to the principle of conservation of energy, a particle cannot overcome an obstacle if it does not have enough energy. For example, if we take a tennis ball and hit it against a wall, which is a potential energy barrier, the ball will reverse its motion and come back. In quantum mechanics, a particle, which as we will see in section 6.3 has both wave and particle behavior, has a non-zero probability of crossing an arbitrarily high potential energy barrier. A wave function is associated with the particle, whose square module represents a probability, in our case the probability of finding the particle in a given region of space. If we consider a one-dimensional potential barrier, the solution of *Schrödinger's equation*[1] inside the barrier is a decreasing function that never becomes zero. There is therefore a certain probability that the particle will cross the barrier.

Guth's inflation theory (see Fig. 4.2) has problems determining the end of inflation. The decay of the inflationary field, the inflaton, follows the rules of quantum mechanics. The beginning is not predictable, and the decay occurs at different times in different places, in the form of bubbles of true vacuum in the false vacuum. The energy released by the decay

---

[1] The Schrödinger equation is an equation of quantum mechanics that allows you to determine the temporal evolution of the state of a system such as a particle or an atom. The unknown factor of this equation called *wave function* is related to the probability of finding a particle in a given spatial region.

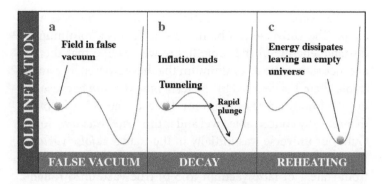

Figure 4.2.  Description of Guth's inflation.

is concentrated in the surface of the bubbles and the collision between bubbles would release energy, in the form of heat, in a chaotic process that would have produced the same amount of inhomogeneity that inflation is supposed to eliminate. The problem was studied by several cosmologists who thought of a pattern in which the bubbles did not collide and were enlarged to a size greater than that of the observed Universe. This led to variants of Guth's inflation, such as eternal inflation.

## 4.2  Other Models for Inflation

The model was replaced by another (Linde, Steinhardt) in which inflation was slower, and exponential expansion does not occur (as in Guth's inflation) when the field is trapped in the false vacuum. However, the idea had some points of contact with Guth's inflation. It was assumed that there was a field similar to that of Higgs or that of the quintessence, a scalar field, called inflaton, and that the universe was initially in a state of false vacuum of this field. This field was the only field then present, distributed throughout the space similar to the Higgs field and with an energetic profile (potential energy), as seen in Fig. 4.3, similar to that of the Higgs field, i.e., the initial part of the profile of the field, corresponding to the false vacuum, is flat as can be seen clearly in Figure 4.3. As is evident, the entrapment of the field in a sort of minimum

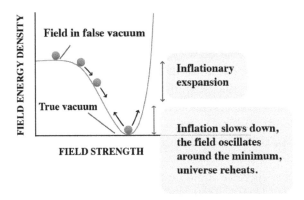

Figure 4.3.    Evolution of the inflationary field.

of false vacuum is not observed as shown in the initial part of Fig. 4.2. Therefore, the tunneling typical of the Guth model was no longer necessary.

From the state of false vacuum, i.e., from the maximum of the curve, the field would have moved with a *slow rolling* (Fig. 4.3) towards the true vacuum, the minimum of the curve, i.e., the region of minimum energy, characterized by repulsive gravity.

This would cause a rapid expansion of space. The field would then continue its rolling phase towards true vacuum (minimum of the curve). The energy at the top, in the false vacuum, is greater than that in the area of minimum, the true vacuum. When the field reaches the minimum of the potential, in the state of true vacuum, it begins to oscillate around it, like a ball dropped down a slope with the shape of the potential profile shown. In this way it would begin to dissipate the energy it had at the top of the curve. The release of energy, according to the dictates of quantum mechanics, produces fields and particles linked to them in the so-called *reheating* phase. Today's particles therefore originated in this phase of the inflaton's evolution (Figure 4.3). After reaching the minimum of the potential, that is the real vacuum, the pace of expansion would have slowed down to today's rates.

In summary, the Universe was full of the inflaton field which was in a state of false vacuum. Quantum fluctuations made the universe come out of the state of false vacuum pushing it to move towards the state of real vacuum. This initially happened slowly, in the slow rolling phase, in which the universe was enormously expanded from dimensions of the order of $10^{-28}$ m$^2$ to a few tens of centimeters in the time it took for the field to reach the minimum of potential. This dimension is the observable universe. According to Guth, the size of the Universe could be $10^{23}$ times larger than that of the observable Universe but there are much larger, and smaller, estimates. At this point, fields and particles were generated and the region in which inflation occurred began to expand with today's pace.

Like all fields, the inflaton field is subject to quantum fluctuations. Quantum fluctuations cause the potential of the inflaton to be subject to uncertainty, which means that inflation cannot end anywhere at the same instant, because the fluctuations give different values to the field even in two very close regions. So, inflation would end at different times at different points. At points where quantum fluctuations exceed a certain threshold, inflation will occur and in the one below the threshold it would stop. A bubble of energy and matter would be created which would give rise to a new universe. Once inflation begins, there will always be an exponentially expanding region that will originate another Universe. This is one of the variants of inflation, *eternal inflation*, in which expansion continues forever in different regions of the universe.

Andrei Linde proposed a theory based on eternal inflation, called *chaotic inflation* or *bubble theory*, which can be described as follows.

As already mentioned, the Universe was initially in a false vacuum. The false vacuum causes a rapid acceleration of the Universe, and transits into the state of true vacuum.

---

[2] At $10^{-36}$ s the cosmological horizon had a dimension of d = 2 c t, where c is the speed of light and t the time.

Figure 4.4.  Eternal inflation. The blue colored area is an inflationary expanding portion of the Universe. The white areas represent bubbles of true
vacuum and are non-contacting universes with different physical characteristics.

The expansion of space was superluminal and therefore a
region that was transformed into a real vacuum was unable to
communicate its state with its neighbors. So, if a region close
to ours was transformed into a real vacuum region, since the
expansion of space is superluminal, the two regions had no
knowledge of each other, they were randomly disconnected,
forming two bubble universes (Fig. 4.4).

We can describe the events by following what happens to
the field (ball), shown in Fig. 4.3. In the descent phase of the
field, in the passage of the field from the false vacuum to the
true vacuum, a "bubble" of the true vacuum (white area) is
formed in the false vacuum (blue region) (Fig. 4.4).

But in the descent the ball can randomly arrive at a generic
point of the potential minimum. Consequently, in each
region, the value of the vacuum energy will be different. So
many bubbles of true vacuum will form, not just one (Fig. 4.4),
and each bubble corresponds to a universe. In other words,
inflation ends at different instants at different points and it is
possible that in some regions it will repeat itself generating
an infinity of universes, a *multiverse*. The bubbles that have
formed expand at a frenzied pace, at the speed of light. Despite
this, they never manage to fill the space because it expands at
a higher rate.

Although a huge number of bubbles (universes) are
created, if there is only one state of false vacuum and one

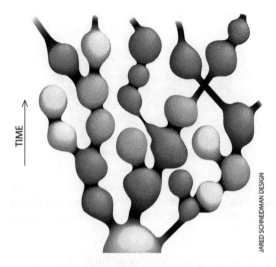

Figure 4.5.   Universe formation in bubble theory. Each universe has different physical laws as shown by the different colors. Source: Jared Schneidman, Scientific American.

of true vacuum, we find ourselves in the condition of the *quantum multiverse*: a large number of universes with the same physical laws. In chaotic inflation, universes exist in a large number of false vacuums and each of them gives rise to different laws of physics, as shown in Fig. 4.5 by the different colors that each bubble has. Each of these bubble universes will be at enormous distances from the others and will not be able to communicate with them.

One of the questions that can be asked is what experimental evidence the theory of inflation has, whether we are sure that it existed or not. In chapter 5, we will discuss the limits on knowledge related to the early Universe and discuss what we know for sure about inflation.

## Summary: Keynotes

- Standard cosmology presents a series of problems such as the problem of flatness, the problem of the horizon, the problem of monopoles. These problems can be solved by assuming that there was a period of exponential expansion in the period $10^{-35}$-$10^{-32}$ s, called inflation.

- There are several models of inflation. Some of them, such as chaotic inflation, predict a continuous generation of universes (multiverse) that will last forever. It must be remembered here that the inflation theory, from the very first (Guth's inflation) had problems in putting an end to the inflation phase. The generation of the multiverse could arise from this problem.

CHAPTER 5

# WHAT DO WE REALLY KNOW ABOUT THE PRIMORDIAL UNIVERSE?

*"The greatest enemy*
*of knowledge is not ignorance; it is*
*the illusion of knowledge."*

— S. Hawking

With the accelerators we have today we can go back to the first billionth of a second ($10^{-12}$ s), in which the universe is made up of a plasma of quarks, leptons and gluons. This quark soup called *quark-gluon plasma* was first observed at Brookhaven National Laboratory in 2002. Discussions about the Universe prior to this time are based on speculative ideas. Ideas such as GUT that occurred well before $10^{-12}$ s are based on well understood, *but in any case, speculative*, physical concepts. If we then venture into the Planck era the situation is even worse because the physics to describe what happened in that era has not yet been formulated: we need to quantize gravity.

Jim Peebles Nobel Prize in Physics in 2019, one of the key architects of physical cosmology, who studies the origin of the Universe, its structure and evolution, pointed out that in reality we do not have a good theory of the origin of the universe. In his words, already quoted

It's very unfortunate that one thinks of the beginning whereas in fact, we have no good theory of such a thing as the beginning....

On the contrary, we have a well-tested theory of the first seconds after the Big Bang that left remains, "fossils", of what happened: the initial state of plasma, the formation of helium and hydrogen nuclei, etc. Instead, if we think of the early stages of the Universe, as Peebles says we only have theories

> We don't have a strong test of what happened earlier in time.... We have theories, but not tested... Any bright physicist can make up theories. They could have nothing to do with reality...You discover which theories are close to reality by comparing to experiments. We just don't have experimental evidence of what happened earlier.

It is therefore essential to discuss the various theories relating to periods prior to the period in which the Universe was made up of the previously mentioned quark-gluon plasma soup. We can start with the inflation that occurred about $10^{-35}$ seconds after the Big Bang.

## 5.1 Pros and Cons of Inflation: Did Inflation Really Exist?

What experimental evidence does the theory of inflation have? There are several, but it must be remembered that inflation was built precisely to explain the observations.

- Inflation provides that the universe is flat, i.e., that the density parameter, $\Omega$, the ratio between the density of the universe and the critical density, is equal to one, $\Omega \approx 1$. If this were not the case and if for example $\Omega$ were greater than 1, the universe would collapse immediately after the Big Bang. If $\Omega < 1$ were found, the universe would expand too fast. We have already seen, when we talked about the *flatness problem* that if today the density of the Universe differed by less than 1% from the critical one, in the early Universe the deviation should be less than one part in $10^{61}$. That is, there is a fine-tuning , relative to the value of the density of the Universe. If the density were to deviate by a very small amount from the critical one, today the

Universe we observe would not exist. The observations of the CMB confirm this prediction. Furthermore, since the universe is flat, its energy is zero and therefore it could have formed from nothing (quantum vacuum), as we will see. To have more certainty on this and to open the door of the Planck era, we need a theory of quantum gravity. There are currently two competing theories attempting to combine gravity and quantum mechanics. One is string theory or more precisely *superstring theory*. This theory, as better described in section 5.5, is a possible theory of everything, in which particles are generated by the vibrations of tiny strings. The other is the *loop quantum gravity* already mentioned.

- Like all quantum fields, the inflaton is subjected to continuous quantum fluctuations. So, there will be regions that will come out of inflation first and others later. At the end of inflation, small differences in energy and density remain. These small fluctuations in density grow due to gravity and are the seeds from which the structures were formed. Inflation predicts a spectrum of perturbations with characteristics that have been confirmed by the CMB study[1].

- Another of the inflation predictions is the production of *primordial gravitational waves,* called *B modes of polarization,* that should have left a mark on the CMB map. The magnitude of these disturbances could be a direct measure of the energy scale at which inflation occurred, thus indicating the energy of the particle, called inflaton, which originated it. In 2014, in an experiment in Antarctica, carried out with the BICEP2 instrument, the signs of the generation of primordial gravitational waves were apparently observed, then disproved by the studies of the PLANCK satellite.

- Inflation gives rise to a homogeneous and isotropic universe like the one observed.

---

[1] Technically we speak of spectral index, Gaussianity, adiabaticity.

Inflation explains many things but leaves many things unexplained. For example, nothing is known about the field that originated it, the inflaton, that someone has proposed is the Higgs field. In order to have an inflation that explains all the things we have said, it is necessary that the conditions that produced it were *finely tuned*. According to Paul Steinhardt, one of the fathers of the theory, if the initial conditions are chosen randomly, it is more likely to obtain "bad" inflation, that is, inflation not able to lead to the current Universe. To be certain about inflation it is necessary to reveal the gravitational waves, of the *first type*, produced by the "stretching" of the space of the inflationary phase and of the *second type gravitational waves* produced by the re-heating phase, which would be the proof, the "smoking gun ", that the inflationary paradigm is correct. Those of the first type would have left marks on the CMB, but as mentioned, although the BICEP2 instrument seemed to have observed them, in reality it was an error. Those of the second type of much greater amplitude have a frequency spectrum that exceeds the sensitivity threshold of current instruments.

So, the inflation theory, although it makes some predictions in accordance with the observations, has not been fully verified and there is a part of the scientific community that does not accept it. Critics argue that this is an undetectable and therefore unscientific theory. Paul Steinhardt, one of the founders of the theory, is very critical of it. Steinhardt disagrees with the idea of the continuous birth of universes predicted by theory. This is why he thought of finding an alternative to inflation, creating the so-called *ecpirotic universe*[2]. The *superstring theory*, in addition to containing small vibrating strings, as described in Section 5.5, predicts the existence of membrane-like structures, called *branes* (see Fig. 5.1).

Steinhardt and Turok imagined, in superstring theory, two *brane universes*, each of which consisted of nine spatial

---

[2] This term can be translated as "transformation into fire" or "going out of fire", a term that in Stoic philosophy indicated the moment in which the world was cyclically created and destroyed.

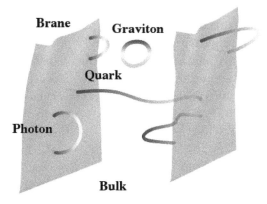

Figure 5.1.    Brane world. The open strings attached to the branes correspond to the material particles and to the electroweak and strong interactions. Open strings are the carriers of the gravitational interaction that can
move in the volume (*bulk*) between the branes.

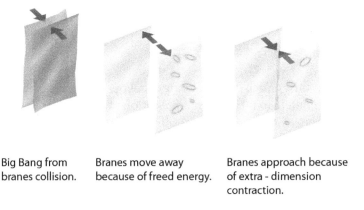

Big Bang from         Branes move away         Branes approach because
branes collision.     because of freed energy.  of extra - dimension
                                                contraction.

Figure 5.2.    Ecpirotic universe.

dimensions. Only three of the nine dimensions were visible and the others
were compacted, rolled up so that they were not visible. The universes were
immersed in a space of greater dimensions, to be precise 10 dimensions,
called *bulk*. The two branes were linked together by a closed string, which
carries gravity, and divided by an extra dimension that could contract
periodically (Fig. 5.2). Since the gravitational force, and the particle that
mediates the interaction, the *graviton*, propagates between two branes,
and given the contraction of the extra dimension, the two brane universes

attract each other giving rise to a collision called *Big Splat* (see Fig. 5.2). Unlike traditional models of the oscillating universe, the ecpirotic universe does not foresee a contraction and therefore an inversion of the arrow of time to reduce entropy.

The entropy problem (present in classical oscillating universes, in which after each collapse is originated an universe of larger dimensions and entropy) is solved, in the authors' description, as follows

> *In the new cyclical model, only the extra dimension shrinks. Entropy is created in branes — for example, when branes collide or when galaxies and stars are formed — then it spreads finely during the rest of the expansion period. The acceleration of the expansion due to dark energy causes, in a particularly effective way, that gravity can make way for the new entropy, so the concentration of entropy on the branes remains low. So, the branes continue to expand even during the contraction phase — in which, only the extra dimension contracts — and the entropy on the branes is never concentrated*

In this model, dark matter and energy are also explained. Dark matter would be the manifestation of the force of gravity of another brane and of the ordinary matter it contains. The collision between the branes would produce enormous energy and heat that generating a gigantic explosion would give rise to a new universe in accelerated expansion. The latter would originate from the residual dark energy of the collision. After the Big Splat the branes move away and return to approach each other, due to gravity and the cyclic contraction of the extra dimension, giving rise to a new cycle. Unlike the classic model of the Big Bang and inflation, the ecpirotic model completely eliminates the singularity. Dark energy is a kind of extra gravity that among other things keeps the branes aligned. The branes are not rigid, but they are like sheets in the wind (see Figure 5.2), so the clash occurs at different points and instants. At the points where it first occurs, the matter and energy produced by the collision thin out due to the expansion. In the points where the collision occurs later, the inhomogeneities that will give rise to the galaxies originate. So, the initial inhomogeneity from which the galaxies originated does not require inflation to be explained, it is an integral part of the model. Is reality better described by inflation or by the model described above? To find out, we need to make comparisons between the predictions of the two theories and the observations. Inflation predicts that on the CMB there are signs of accelerated expansion: the so-called *B modes,* already mentioned, due to the generation of gravitational waves during inflation. The ecpirotic model does not foresee them. As already mentioned, in 2014, the BICEP-2 experiment seemed to have found this effect. Unfortunately, this result was soon disproved and therefore inflation and the ecpirotic universe were both put back into the race. It must be said that Linde and collaborators have shown that the ecpirotic universe has a series of inconsistencies with the *M* theory. For this reason, Steinhardt and Turok added more precise details and also changed the name of the model to *the phoenix universe.* The studies on this model have continued until arriving at two different possible models, one based on quantum mechanics, proposed by Turok and Gielen, and a classical model proposed by Steinhardt. In both, the singularity is avoided by obtaining the *Big Bounce*[3] (see Fig. 9.1). Then, the Universe could have started with a Big Bang, and then inflation, or with a Big Bounce. The theories that favor a Big Bounce are *superstring theory,* and the *loop quantum gravity.* As seen in the case of the ecpirotic Universe, the B modes can help to disentangle between that model and inflation. Recently Xian Cheng, Abraham Loeb, and Zhong-Zhi Xianyu, showed that a way to distinguish between inflation and a Big Bounce is to use *"clock signals",* wiggle-like features that can be observed in the matter and energy distribution on cosmic distance scales. In the

---

[3] It is a model in which the universe will expand to a maximum and then contract to produce a very dense and hot universe as in the case of the Big Bang, but avoiding the gravitational singularity, and then "bouncing" (*Big Bounce*) giving rise to a new expansion.

primordial Universe, massive fields behaves as standard clocks, leaving an imprint in the density perturbations that may allow to disentangle between the Big Bounce and inflation. This is a promising test for the future.

Another critic of inflation comes from the Nobel laureate Sir Roger Penrose, according to whom inflation is a "fantasy"

> *It is used to explain why the Universe is uniform and flat... But we need a physics invented ad hoc, starting with the inflaton, a particle whose existence is only needed to justify inflation. It is an "artificial" theory, which does not solve the fundamental problem concerning the origin of the Universe ...*

Even the Nobel Prize in Physics of 2019, Jim Peebles, points the finger at inflation and the lack of data we have. Using his own words

> *"It's a beautiful theory. Many people think it's so beautiful that it's surely right. But its evidence is very sparse.*

As mentioned earlier, inflation makes a series of predictions, but in reality, we cannot speak of true predictions because the theory is built ad hoc to solve the problems we have talked about. As argued by Steinhardt and Penrose, the theory is not really falsifiable since its parameters are too flexible for real experimental verification. By appropriately varying the parameters it is possible to include any experimental test in the theory. This is a first criticism of the model. A second criticism is that the conditions necessary for the inflationary phase to begin are unlikely, they require fine-tuning. Another criticism is that inflation (at least in the case of eternal inflation) leads, as seen, to the formation of a huge number of universes, the multiverse, and not all physicists are willing to accept its existence. Ultimately, although many cosmologists believe in the theory of inflation, certain proofs of its existence have not yet been found. Such evidence could come from the cosmic microwave background, the CMB which is a powerful laboratory for cosmology. Massive observational efforts have been made to try to reveal the signs of primordial gravitational waves. The answer could come from tools such as BICEP and QUIJOTE or from future satellites that have been proposed: PIXIE, LiteBIRD, JAXA, CORE. A more in-depth study by the CMB will provide us with new ways to study the thermal history of the universe and inflation.

## 5.2 The Great Unification

In physics there is a sort of aesthetic sense that pushes us to seek a unified description of phenomena. The first unification of physics dates back to the seventeenth century when Newton intuited that the force that causes the bodies to fall is the same one that produces the motion of the Moon around the Earth. A second unification occurred when James Clerck Maxwell unified electricity, magnetism and optics. As already mentioned, in the 70s of the last century it was shown how the electromagnetic force and the weak one above a certain energy unite in the electroweak interaction. The standard model also allows us to describe the strong interaction. There are ideas on how strong interaction can be unified with both electromagnetism and weak interaction. We talk about the *Grand Unified Theory* (GUT). Among other things, we have seen that the standard model is a very successful theory, but several open questions remain, which could be dissolved by theories beyond the standard model. The GUT is one of these "*beyond the standard model*" theories. A common feature of the GUT is that in it the electromagnetic force, the strong nuclear force and the weak nuclear force must be aspects of the same interaction, in other words they must be unified and must have the same *mediator boson* for all. At low energies, i.e., energies below $10^{15}$ GeV[4], the GUT shows three different types of interaction (electromagnetic interaction, strong nuclear interaction and weak nuclear interaction). When the energy reaches $10^{15}$ GeV, the unifying energy, the three interactions are

---

[4] Corresponding approximately to the kinetic energy of a 1000 kg car at a speed of 100 km/h.

transformed into a single one. The most powerful accelerator in the world reaches an energy of 14 TeV (14000 GeV), much lower than the energy of the GUT, so there are practical problems in verifying or disproving the GUT theories. However, it is possible to evaluate the validity of the GUTs indirectly, through some predictions of the theories such as the decay of the proton or the existence of magnetic monopoles. The latter are the equivalent of electrical charges. In fact, the magnetic fields observed always have two polarities and so far, a magnetic field with only one pole has never been observed. Some Grand Unification (GUT) theories, such as the Georgi-Glashow model, predict proton decay. These would have a *half-life*[5] of the order of $10^{30}$ years. One of the possibilities of proton decay is that it decays into a positron, a neutral pion and 2 photons. The most recent experiment that studies this problem is that of SuperKamiokande containing 50,000 tons of ultra-pure water containing $10^{34}$ protons and more than 11,000 photomultipliers that reveal the blue light produced by the *Cherenkov effect*[6]. According to the experiment, the half-life of the proton must be greater than $10^{33}$ years. The results of the SuperKamiokande, do not say that the proton does not decay but only give a lower limit to its half-life. So maybe the protons will decay in more than $10^{34}$ years, or maybe they won't decay. The results of the SuperKamiokande refute the validity of Georgi-Glashow's GUT, however there are others in which the proton is longer-lived. As for monopoles, they have never been observed and this is yet another point against the GUTs. To these problems we must add the fact that GUTs neglect gravity, which implies that the GUTs would not be complete. We need a theory of unification between quantum mechanics and gravity. As we saw in Chapter 2, the conditions under which GUT would occur in the early Universe correspond to a period between $10^{-43}$ s to $10^{-36}$ s and temperatures of the order

---

[5] The half-life is the time it takes for the number of protons, or another radioactive element, to be reduced by half.

[6] When a particle moves in a medium faster than the speed of light in the medium, a cone-shaped flash of light is emitted with apex in the particle.

of $10^{30}$ K. At the end of the GUT epoch, when the temperature reaches $10^{28}$ K, the Universe is subject to the decoupling of the strong interaction from the electroweak force (consisting of the electromagnetic force and the weak force) which will constitute two separate forces. This phase is called the *grand unification phase transition*. As we have said previously, there is no experimental evidence of the existence of GUT. In other words, the time between $10^{-43}$ s to $10^{-36}$, which we have called GUT, is just a speculation, a leap of faith by physicists whose equations say that with increasing energy interactions tend to unify. The GUT is a kind of conceptual extrapolation of the theory of the unification of the electromagnetic force and the weak force discovered by Sheldon Glashow, Steven Weinberg and Abdus Salam and experimentally observed at 246 GeV. The problem is that while the electroweak unification has been observed experimentally, the GUT has never been, because, as mentioned, the energies involved are much higher than those of the most powerful accelerator we have, the LHC. In other words, we have no experimental evidence that a phase of great unification can exist in the universe. There is another problem to highlight. The intensity of the elementary interactions is not constant but depends on the energy. Figure 5.3 shows how the intensity of the strong, weak and electromagnetic interactions vary with energy. As we can see, the intensities tend to converge towards a sort of unification. We must remember here that the

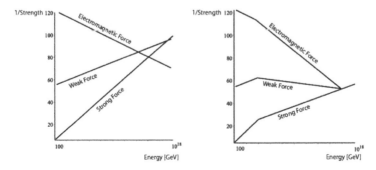

Figure 5.3. Unification of interactions with supersymmetry (left) and without supersymmetry (right).

curves of the various forces are supported by experiments only up to the electroweak epoch.

In the box on the left we see that at $10^{15}$ GeV the three forces do not unite at one point, i.e., there is no true unification. If you want the three curves to unite at one point and have the unification, as shown in the right panel of Figure 5.3, one must take into account an extension of the standard model: the *supersymmetric model* (SUSY) which at each particle matches its supersymmetric particle or s-particle. For example, in the case of bosons, the supersymmetric companions are fermions, and vice versa.

To give some examples, the photon corresponds to the *photino*, the gluon to the *gluino*, the Z particle to the *zino*, the W particle to the *wino*, the graviton to the *gravitino*, the Higgs particle to the *higgsino*. The supersymmetric companions of the fermions are bosons which are indicated by the name of the corresponding fermion preceded by an s. For example, the electron corresponds to the *s-electron*, the neutrino to the *s-neutrino*, the quarks to the *s-quarks*. Now if in the ordinary world of low energies, we observe only usual, non-supersymmetric particles, this means that there is a limit energy above which the world is supersymmetric and below it we have the ordinary world with ordinary particles. For theoretical reasons that we do not discuss here this scale is expected to be not much larger than the *electroweak scale*, i.e., a few hundred GeV. Unfortunately, experiments show that this is not the case. Research with the LHC did not see any signs of supersymmetry and supersymmetric particles. This is another problem for the GUT.

Finally, the same aesthetic sense that pushes us to seek a unified description of phenomena makes us go beyond the GUT. It is thought that all interactions can be unified at energies of the order of $10^{19}$ GeV. The theory that does this is called the *theory of everything* (TOE) (see Fig. 5.4).

## 5.3 Quantum Gravity

Inflation occurred at times of the order of $10^{-35}$ s after the big bang and transformed a tiny region of space in the observable

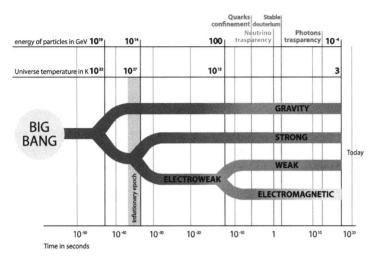

Figure 5.4.    Unification of interactions. Source: INFN, Science for all

Universe. Such a region of space must have already existed in earlier times. An attempt to study what happened before inflation, opening a window on the Planck era, the period between $10^{-43}$ s and time zero, runs into a big problem. We don't have a theory describing this era. Gravity is a very weak force. Today it is $10^{36}$ times weaker than the electromagnetic force and $10^{38}$ times less than the strong interaction. As the temperature increases, going back in time, the interactions tend to unify, that is, to have the same value. At the time of the great unification (GUT) the Universe had a temperature of the order of $10^{30}$ K and the strong and electroweak interaction constituted of a single interaction. It is believed that in Planck's time gravity was also unified with other forces (Theory of Everything, TOE). This implies that the intensity of gravity was equal to that of the other interactions and general relativity alone could no longer describe how gravity behaved. The mechanical effects must be taken into account. To describe the Planck epoch we therefore need a new theory called *quantum gravity*, which we do not yet have. Quantizing gravity is an extremely complex problem. A first step in this direction is the semiclassical approach. In this approach, the so-called *degrees of freedom* are treated in a classical (non-quantum) manner and the quantum evolution of fields in classical curved space-time. An important result of this approach is the *Hawking radiation* (see next section) associated with black holes. As for research on quantum gravity, several paths have been followed. One of the approaches to obtain a quantum theory of gravity is that of the unification of interactions in nature. One way followed is to geometrize non-gravitational interactions by adding other compacted spatial dimensions, as in the *Kaluza-Klein theories*. However, this approach does not appear to be very promising. The other way is to ignore the geometric character of gravity and treat gravity like other interactions, such as in the theory of superstrings, which we have already spoken about. The mechanism to follow is similar to that used in the case of Quantum Electro-dynamics (QED), the quantum field of the electromagnetic field, or in the case of the Quantum Chromo Dynamics (QCD), the quantum field theory of the strong interaction, assuming the existence of an interaction-carrying particle, the *graviton*, which, however, has never been observed.

Among other things, the graviton, like other particles, is generated by the oscillation of the strings. The graviton, similar to the photon, would have zero mass because gravitational interactions similar to electromagnetic ones have an infinite range, and since the range is inversely proportional to the mass, this must be infinite. Thinking of gravity as if it were a graviton field we have a similar problem, but much worse than what happens in *QED*, the observable quantities diverge, they become infinite. In the case of *QED* there is a technique called *renormalization* that allows to eliminate infinities. Quantum gravity, on the other hand, cannot be renormalized, that is, infinities cannot be canceled. There are other problems if we try to obtain a theory of quantum gravity starting from general relativity.

In fact, if we try to incorporate gravity, treated according to the schemes of general relativity, we must remember that gravity and mass produce the curvature of space-time. In quantum mechanics, space-time is flat as in special relativity and behaves like a passive scenario. On the other hand, in general relativity space plays an active role and has a dynamic behavior. This is just one of the problems encountered in trying to "marry" relativity and quantum mechanics. However, the ultimate goal is to incorporate gravity into the standard model or to transform gravity into a field theory. The main avenues followed to achieve quantum gravity are the *superstring theory* on which great hopes were placed, but today it does not seem to be able to deliver what it promised. The other possibility is the theory of *loop quantum gravity*, already mentioned.

## 5.4 Loop Quantum Gravity

The theory of loop quantum gravity (LQG) abandons the idea that space is the scenario in which physical theories are developed. The theory is formulated as a quantum field theory that does not need space. Among the most important characteristics of this theory there is the discrete character of the geometric quantities (e.g., length and area) that form space-time.

The theory predicts the existence of a minimum length, the Planck length. The result is a discrete geometry composed of "space-time atoms", called *spin networks*. They constitute the quantum states of the gravitational field. Since spin networks are quantum states, to study their evolution we must follow the rules of quantum mechanics. The succession of intermediate states between two spin networks constitutes the *spin foam*. In theory, space is quantized on the Planck length scale, below which space is no longer continuous.

The theory is based on a rewrite of Einstein's equations by Abhay Ashtekar. Starting from Roger Penrose's concept of spin networks, Carlo Rovelli and Lee Smolin created a quantum theory of gravity. Unlike superstring theory, it does not include supersymmetry and works with the usual 4 dimensions (3 spatial plus one temporal dimension). One of the successes of this theory is the reproduction of the effect of the evaporation of black holes obtained by Stephen Hawking, the *Hawking radiation*. A black hole is generated by the collapse of a large-mass star in an infinitely small region called a *singularity*.

Around there is a region called the *event horizon* from which not even light can escape. If an object falls into the black hole, the event horizon tends to increase (or at least not to decrease). Since in nature there is a quantity that tends to increase or at most to remain constant, i.e., entropy, in 1972 Jacob Bekenstein hypothesized that the entropy of a black hole was proportional to the event horizon. In 1974 Stephen Hawking demonstrated the proportionality between entropy and the surface of the event horizon, the Bekenstein-Hawking formula and finally determined a relationship between temperature and mass of the black hole. In this way he showed that black holes were not so black and could emit radiation. As already mentioned, the calculation was done in the semiclassical approximation of quantum gravity. That is, moving a little away from the black hole, the effects of relativity weaken and can be combined with those of quantum mechanics. How does the black hole radiate and lose mass? The Hawking radiation phenomenon can be simplified like this. In the vacuum around the black hole, virtual particles and antiparticles appear and disappear. Due to the huge gravitational field of the black hole, one of the particles of the pair could fall into the black hole leaving the other free particle outside. This is equivalent to the creation of particles of mass equivalent to the mass of the particle left outside the black hole, at the expense of its energy. Particles moving away from the black hole behave like thermal radiation leaving a body at a non-zero temperature.

Consequently, the black hole will slowly lose mass, in times proportional to the cube of its mass; for example, a black hole of a solar mass takes $10^{67}$ years to evaporate. Its temperature will also increase inversely proportional to its mass. Using the quantum loop theory, the equation that links entropy with the surface of the event horizon can be obtained. Further studies led by Jorge Pullin have come to the conclusion that the center of the black hole would not be a singularity with infinite gravity, but finite and it would be possible to move to another place in the Universe or to another Universe.

When it is applied to the Universe it gives results in some ways similar to string theory, which we will see in a moment.

According to LQG, space-time is made up of regions of $10^{-35}$ m in size, which can contain a finite amount of energy. So as in the theory of superstring there is a minimum dimension under which we cannot go down. In loop quantum theory, space is discrete. This theory, similarly, to the superstring theory, does not admit the singularity of the Big Bang. The predicted universe is a variant of the oscillating universe. The universe expands to a maximum and then collapses again. We pass from a pre-universe of eternal duration, a rebound at initial time ($t = 0$), and an infinite universe. The Universe described by the theory has no beginning or end. Tests have been devised to verify the theory developed so far. According to one of the models, photons with different energies move at different speeds. The so-called *gamma ray bursts*, very energetic flashes emitted in the gamma area of the spectrum were used to check if the prediction is correct. These events occur when a star of enormous mass and rotating collapses on itself, emitting an enormous amount of energy, equal to that emitted by the Sun in ten billion years. A team led by Robert Nemiroff used the Fermi satellite to test the theory's prediction. They observed three gamma rays of different energies arrived at the detector at different instants. After several studies, the researchers concluded that the most likely thing is that the photons traveled the distance together to us and that they were not deflected in their path. In the evaluation, however, we must also take into account the effect of objects (stars, dust) that could have deflected photons and of the *quantum foam* that makes up space-time. By observing no deviations, the researchers concluded that quantum foam does not exist. In reality, the research did not take into account a series of physical effects, as shown by the physicist Giovanni Amelino-Camelia and therefore another experiment is needed to confirm the result. Another possibility would be the observation of a *"rainbow"* produced by space-time. As light passing through a prism gives rise to a rainbow, so particles with different energies perceive space-time as having different structures. Jerzy Lewandowski would seem to have thought of a mechanism to make this space-time rainbow appear. Another way to verify quantum gravity is gravitational waves, the B modes, which we talked about in Section 5.1. Having originated in times when the effects of quantum gravity were important and therefore their detection would be observational evidence of the quantum nature of gravity. Another way of verifying the theory is to verify whether two macroscopic objects with masses of the order of the nanogram ($10^{-9}$ g) can become quantum-mechanically entangled with each other through mutual gravitational attraction. As we will see in Section 6.7, *entanglement* is a quantum phenomenon in which two particles become inseparably intertwined, that is, they share a single physical description (a single wave function) that specifies their combined states. The two objects can remain entangled, only if the force acting between them, that in our case is gravity, is a quantum interaction mediated by gravitons. However, eminent physicists such as Freeman Dyson, think that quantum gravity does not exist, and that gravity is a purely classical field in the universe. Roger Penrose also comes to similar conclusions. In conclusion, LQG is an interesting theory, but it is still under development. It is unclear whether it will allow the construction of full quantum gravity. At the same time, it is also not clear whether quantum gravity can exist in nature.

## 5.5 The Theory of Superstrings

As mentioned, one of the fundamental objectives of modern physics is the search for a *theory of everything* that should bring together all interactions in a single framework. Although it is possible that it does not exist, there is still a kind of aesthetic sense that prompts us to seek such a unified description of phenomena. This research was initiated and not completed by Einstein who was followed by several generations of physicists. In 1919, four years after the publication of General Relativity, Theodor Kaluza proposed a theory of unification of electromagnetism and General Relativity in a five-dimensional space, formed by four spatial dimensions and one temporal. Kaluza sent the study to Einstein who initially did not understand the role of the fourth spatial dimension, but then did his utmost to present it first in 1918 at the Berlin Academy of Sciences and then to have it published in 1921. In 1926 Klein expanded the study by introducing quantum concepts, managing to explain the quantization of the electric charge based on the quantization of the moment in the extra dimension and also calculated the order of magnitude of the extra dimension, which must have been about $10^{-22}$ m. After an initial interest in the Kaluza-Klein theory, it was almost forgotten, until the 1970s. A descendant of the Kaluza-Klein theory in a decadimensional space is the *superstring theory*, which is proposed as a possible theory of everything, in which particles are generated by the vibrations of tiny $10^{-35}$ m strings. String theory initially included only bosons, in 26 dimensions, and was a theory of strong interactions. Later, Ramond, Neveu, and Schwarz showed how to introduce fermions. The connection of the theory with supersymmetry led to the superstring theory. Furthermore, in 1974 Scherk and Schwarz pointed out that superstring theory, rather than a theory of strong interactions, was a theory of quantum gravity and more generally a theory of everything. One problem with the theory is that it works in 10 dimensional spaces (9 spatial plus 1 temporal dimension), and our world has at most four dimensions (3 spatial and one temporal dimension). Where are the dimensions we don't see? As Klein had already explained, the extra dimensions are compact, closed in on themselves and extremely small in size. To explain the idea of extra dimension, let's consider a long cylinder, or a rope, which has two dimensions. If we observe the cylinder from a great distance, we will perceive it as a one-dimensional wire. To see the extra dimension, you have to look at it closely.

A tightrope walker can only move in one dimension, back and forth, but an ant can also go around the wire, that is, around the base circle (Figure 5.5).

You can have only one extra dimension or more than one that can also have periodic properties.

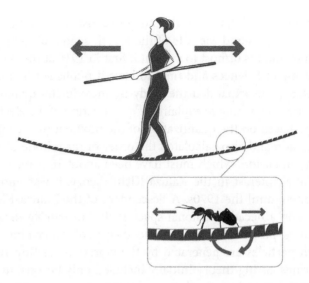

Figure 5.5.   an example of the concept of extra dimensions. For a tightrope walker, the wire has only one dimension, but for an ant it has two, because it can go around it.

There are 5 different superstring theories and they can be considered as 5 different aspects of a single theory called *M theory*, in an 11-dimensional space. The *M theory* was introduced by Edward Witten in 1995, in the so-called "second string revolution". The curious thing is that it is not known what the M indicates because Witten never revealed it. Another interesting point is that, as noted by Joseph Polchinsky, string theory predicts and requires, due to its consistency, the existence of larger objects such as *D-branes*. For example, a 2-brane is a membrane, a 0-brane is a particle, and a 1-brane is a string. The extension of string theory to branes has complicated the *compactification problem* even more, as it has led to the discovery of other ways to compact extra dimensions. According to some researchers, our universe could be on a 3-brane, having 3 + 1 dimensions, which shakes, like a sheet in the wind, in an environment of higher dimensions.

At this point one might wonder if the superstring theory or rather the M theory is a valid candidate to be a *TOE*. The answer is certainly negative, because it is not complete and only now, we are beginning to understand its basic aspects. The superstring theory made many followers in the early stages and gave hope that it was close to solving the age-old problem of the unification of gravity and quantum mechanics. Time has shown that things are not that trivial. There is little or no evidence even that string theory is a solid scientific theory. It provides for supersymmetry, but the latter was not observed at CERN.

It explains *Hawking radiation*, like *loop quantum gravity*, but this has never been observed. If the proton decays, this would be evidence in favor of supersymmetry, but, as discussed, the proton does not decay, at least for $10^{34}$ years. Supersymmetry predicts dark matter, but this too has never been observed. Other predictions of the theory are the existence of new long-range weak forces, which have also never been observed. It was hoped that the theory could resolve the huge discrepancy between the observed and calculated value of the cosmological constant, a factor of $10^{120}$. Supersymmetry was only able to reduce the discrepancy to values on the order of $10^{50}$ but not to solve the problem. Another problem is related to the number of compactifications which is extremely large, of the order of $10^{500}$, as we will see in chapter 7. With such a large number of compactifications you have a basic problem. Normally when you test a theory you try to see if an observation disprove it or not. In the case of superstring theory, no experiment could disprove it because we could use another compactification and other parameters. So, we get a chameleon theory that can adapt to any result. A theory so flexible that it is not able to predict any phenomenon. However, people in the superstring field do not lose hope and the research continues.

## 5.6 Planck Era

If we continue our trip back in time, we arrive at the period between the beginning (time zero) and $10^{-43}$ s, the so-called Planck epoch. Assuming that we could make this journey to the origin of the Cosmos, the known laws of physics would allow us to understand the universe only up to scales larger than Planck's, about $10^{-35}$ m. At smaller scales we need, as many times said, quantum gravity that doesn't exist yet. In practice, even having formulated this theory, we could understand universe only from theoretical point of view, but we could not observe it with electromagnetic radiation, because from Big Bang to 380000 years after Big Bang matter in universe was so dense that it was completely opaque. It is as if between us and Big Bang there was an impenetrable wall. As we discussed, at Planck time ($10^{-43}$ s) Universe is characterized by pressure, temperature and density so high that space is completely different from what we know. It is extremely distorted and it is thought that due to quantum fluctuations there were regions of space-time having dimensions equal to Planck length ($10^{-35}$ cm) that appeared and disappeared continuously. Such discontinuous and seething structure of space-time is usually referred to as quantum foam. The cosmological horizon was tiny, equal to the Planck length. The conditions of that time are so extreme that they cannot be recreated even in the most powerful particle accelerator in the world, the LHC at CERN. Penetrating the secrets of the Planck epoch is impossible both because we lack the physics theory describing this period and because the energies are too high for our accelerators. If we extrapolate back the conditions at Planck time to the beginning, we would expect time zero to constitute a singularity with diverging density, temperature, etc., However, if we believe the LQG predictions, for example, things are different. The Big Bang would have been a *Big Bounce*. A Universe previous to ours would have contracted reaching a minimum size, according to the LQG and from that point the expansion starts again, as in a Big Bounce. Consequently, there is no singularity and infinite values of density, temperature, etc. .. Not everyone agrees on these conclusions. For example, Neil Turok states that to go back in time to the inflationary phase, researchers need to use a series of "artificial assumptions". Turok warns that

> *loop quantum gravity is interesting, but it is not yet a real theory and therefore we must be careful not to take some of its predictions seriously.*

Believing in the LQG, but also in a generic cyclical theory of the universe, it is practically possible to ask what happened before the Big Bang. We said in section 1.2 that it made no sense to ask what happened before the Big Bang, because time originated from them. In reality, in a cyclic universe, the Big Bounce corresponds to our Big Bang. So, before the Big Bang there was another universe that expanded and eventually collapsed. In conclusion, the Planck era is a mystery. We do not have the physical tools nor is it possible for us to recreate the conditions of what happened at that time on an experimental level. This second aspect is the most critical because we would need a huge accelerator whose construction falls within the scope of science fiction. Going to times close to time zero and concluding that the Universe originates from nothing as we will discuss in chapter 9, is pure speculation.

Ultimately, our knowledge of the early universe before $10^{-12}$ s has big limits that become bigger and bigger as we approach time zero, the Big Bang. We often hear about what happened in the early universe as if those were things that have already been verified and established. The reader is never warned that these are speculative theories. Thus, we speak of the great unification as if it were an era that certainly existed, we speak of the multiverse as something certain, and of a universe born out of nothing with ease, when there is not even a complete theory to deal with this last problem. Remembering the words of Jim Peebles

*we have no good theory of such a thing as the beginning....*

When we talk about the early universe and the theories related to it, we must always remember that nothing is certain.

## Summary: Key Points

- Knowledge about our universe is experimentally limited to $10^{-12}$ s, in previous times the most powerful particle accelerators we have are not energetic enough.

- Inflation occurred much earlier than $10^{-12}$ s. We do not know which agent produced the exponential expansion, we have not revealed the primordial gravitational waves generated in this period and they should be observable on the CMB. The theory has many followers, but we don't have enough data to be sure of its existence.
- An extension of physics beyond the standard model is the GUT. None of the theory's predictions have ever been verified. It is therefore a speculative theory.
- If we go back in time, to Planck's time, in addition to the problems described for inflation and the GUT, another is added: we do not have the physical theory, quantum gravity, necessary to study this period.
- Quantum gravity candidates such as superstring theory or loop gravity have problems. The first, in addition to being incomplete, involves a huge number of compactifications that make it a theory of anything rather than a theory of everything (TOE). The second is incomplete and none of the proposed tests have yet been verified. Some insiders believe that gravity is a purely classical interaction impossible to quantize.
- Discussions relating to the early Universe, before $10^{-12}$ s, devoid of experimental evidence, are only speculations
- Another speculation is that the Universe appeared out of nowhere at time zero, based on theories not yet complete and understood.

# CHAPTER 6

# THE MIRACLES OF QUANTUM MECHANICS

*Things are united by invisible bonds.*
*You can't pick a flower without*
*upsetting a star*

— Galileo Galilei

In "*Exposition du systeme du monde*" (Exposition of the system of the world), in 1796 Pierre Simon de Laplace elaborated (in parallel to Kant) the hypothesis of the origin of the solar system from a primitive nebula. He gave the text to Napoleon who after reading it asked him why God was not mentioned in the whole text. Laplace replied: *Sire, I had no need of that hypothesis*[1]. Laplace's conclusions were based on determinism, the idea that the phenomena that occur in the world are linked to each other by precise cause-effect relationships. In this way of seeing the world, which reigned until the 20th century, probability was excluded and everything could be rigorously described using mathematical and physical laws. The deterministic universe was strictly regulated by causality. Returning to Laplace, he was convinced that using Newton's laws, knowing the initial conditions of the Universe, it was possible to predict every past and future state of the same. In his words

> ....*An intelligence knowing all the forces acting in nature at a given instant, as well as the momentary positions of all things in the universe, would be able to comprehend in one single*

---

[1] It seems that Napoleon meeting Lagrange told him what had happened, to which Lagrange replied: "Ah, but that is a fine hypothesis. It explains so many things".

*formula the motions of the largest bodies as well as the light-est atoms in the world, provided that its intellect were sufficiently powerful to subject all data to analysis; to it nothing would be uncertain, the future as well as the past would be present to its eyes.*

This idea of the world was completely shattered by quantum mechanics. It substituted uncertainty for determinism and brought probability and "strangeness" into physics. Going into quantum rules implies abandoning the intuitive patterns on which our worldview is based, built day after day by our interaction with the macroscopic world. While classical physics gives us a description of the macroscopic world, quantum mechanics is the theory necessary to understand the microscopic world: molecules, atoms, particles. Similar to the special and general theory of relativity that allow us to understand the world when we consider speeds very comparable to that of light or massive objects (e.g., black holes), quantum mechanics extends classical physics to the domain of very small objects, at the level atomic and subatomic. Unlike other theories of physics, quantum mechanics shows us that some fundamental and basic concepts of the macroscopic world completely lose meaning at the atomic and subatomic level.

Although the theory is coherent from a mathematical point of view and that it agrees with the experiments with incredible precision, understanding its inner meaning is extremely difficult if not impossible. In 1965, Richard Feynman was writing

*There was a time when the newspapers said that only twelve men understood the theory of relativity. I do not believe there ever was such a time. There might have been a time when only one man did, because he was the only guy who caught on, before he wrote his paper. But after people read the paper a lot of people understood the theory of relativity in some way or other, certainly more than twelve. On the other hand, I think I can safely say that nobody understands quantum mechanics...*

More than 50 years have passed since Feynman expressed this point of view and still the situation has not changed. Although a myriad of experiments have been carried out, all confirmed, and a large amount of calculations have been developed, the feeling that quantum mechanics is a mysterious theory still remains intact.

## 6.1 Quantum Uncertainty

We can give some examples that show the strangeness of the quantum world. For example, if we play table tennis, tennis, or football, we can follow the motion of the ball, see its trajectory. This is possible because the light made up of photons reflects off the ball and reaches our eye. The mass of a photon is much smaller than that of the ball so the impact of the photon with the ball does not produce any practical effect on the latter. Now let's try to think, that some strange machine shrinks us to a size comparable to atoms and that we can continue our game in the microscopic world, using electrons instead of balls. In this case the trajectories we saw in the microscopic world lose their meaning, they no longer exist. In order to observe the electron, we must always use photons. When these collide, the electrons disturb their motion. The greater the energy of the photons, the more the motion will be disturbed. What happens is similar to what happened in an anecdote, told by Carlo Rovelli that refers to Heisenberg, one of the fathers of quantum mechanics. One evening Heisenberg was walking in the park near the Copenhagen Institute for Theoretical Physics. He saw for a moment a man passing under a lamppost and then see him disappear and then reappear when the man passed under another lamppost. What happened was that the man was visible in the illuminated areas and not visible in the dark ones. It was obvious that an object as large as a man does not have the property of appearing and disappearing, but in the microcosm this could happen. An electron could appear and disappear, making *"quantum leaps"*, for example, between different orbits in an atom. In the microcosm, the trajectory may no longer be a sensible concept. Taking the argument to the extreme, it is possible that an electron exists only when you look at it, that is, when it interacts with a photon. If we want to have a trajectory of the electron, we must know its position and its speed, its motion. To do this, as we said, we have to hit it with a photon. Each photon has its own energy, and a wavelength inversely proportional to the energy: the greater the energy the lower the wavelength, which gives us the region in which the electron is located. So, if we want to know with good precision where the photon is we have to use high-energy photons. If we use a gamma photon, its wavelength will be between $10^{-16}$ and $10^{-12}$ m, and we could locate the electron with great precision, less than a thousand billionths of a meter. So, we know the position of the electron well. And what about its speed? It will be all the more indeterminate the greater the precision with which we know the position of the electron. In other words, the lower the uncertainty about the position, the greater the uncertainty about the motion. There is no way to have precise knowledge of position and speed simultaneously. This problem as we have already seen is known as the *Heisenberg uncertainty principle*. As we have seen, quantities such as position and moment (mass product by velocity) are subject to uncertainty. The greater the precision with which we know one of them, the lower the precision with which we know the other. The uncertainty does not depend on our limits in conducting the experiments, it is intrinsic to nature. Observation changes reality. While in the macroscopic world there is an objective reality, in the microscopic world things are completely different. The attempt to define an objective reality is doomed to fail, since the observer's action changes it into a subjective reality. At the same time this highlight, as we will see better in the following sections, that reality is forged by the observer. So, the world that quantum mechanics shows us is completely different from the one Laplace thought of. The clockwork Laplace's Universe, and Newtonian mechanics is torn to shreds by quantum mechanics. The information relating to an electron or another particle is and will always be incomplete and this has influences on the very future of the particle, which remains inaccessible to us. The uncertainty that prevails in the quantum realm disappears when we move into the macroscopic realm. This is because the dimensions of macroscopic objects are so much larger than microscopic ones that the observation of a component of the macroscopic world will not be disturbed by the interaction with tiny photons.

## 6.2 Creation of Particles and Universes

The uncertainty principle applies to several conjugated variables. In section 4.1 we have seen that energy, $E$, and time, $t$, are also under the tyranny of the uncertainty principle. The shorter the life of a particle, the more uncertain its energy is. We not only have problems in knowing the energy of a system at a given time, but if we needed to know the energy exactly, we would have to wait for an infinite time. This indeterminacy creates an apparent violation of the energy conservation principle. As we have already seen, each region of space is subject to quantum fluctuations. A system does not have a defined energy, it fluctuates continuously. The changes are so fast that they cannot be measured directly. For very short moments, nature allows the principle of energy conservation to be violated. The time in which the violation is possible is the longer the less the energy involved. In addition to these energy fluctuations, *virtual particles* can appear, and they have a very short life, so short that they cannot be measured. A virtual particle cannot appear alone but always appears with a companion, a *virtual antiparticle*. The charge must be conserved, so if an electron appears a positron must also appear. So, matter and antimatter are created for a very short time and then recombine, disappearing and leaving energy behind. We have seen that the appearance of these particles is possible because what we call vacuum is not actually empty but is made up of fields. We have said that virtual particles cannot be detected directly but there are indirect ways to show that they really exist. An example is *Lamb shift*.

In 1928 Dirac obtained an equation that brings together quantum mechanics and special relativity. In 1974 Willis

Lamb and Robert Retherford found a tiny difference in energy between two levels (2 s and 2p) of the hydrogen atom which, according to Dirac's equation, should have had the same energy. This was a big problem since the equation had made very precise predictions and was the best equation available to describe the structure of the atom. Well, the Dirac equation does its job very well, the problem is related to the existence of a vacuum. Due to the fluctuations of the vacuum, particles and antiparticles appear and disappear at every point in a period of time inversely proportional to the energies of the particles created. Pairs of photons are also created. The electrons of the atom that are in the two states called (2s and 2p) have a high probability of being close to the nucleus. The fluctuations of the vacuum move them away from the proton, increasing its energy. Ultimately the void is responsible for the said energetic discrepancy. This effect is called the *Lamb effect* and is of considerable importance because its explanation led to the formulation of quantum electrodynamics. Quantum mechanics can also change the nature of black holes, as we saw in section 5.4. As we know, classic black holes tend to "devour" what passes near them[2].

Taking into account quantum mechanics, black holes can radiate and in this way energy and mass are subtracted from the black hole. As we will see in chapter 9 by combining general relativity and quantum mechanics in a semi-classical way, in *quantum cosmology* it is possible to generate universes. There are works and books that talk about creating universes from nothing. For example, Stephen Hawking and Leonard Mlodinow in "*The Grand Design*" write

> ....*the universe can be created from nothing ...Spontaneous creation is the reason there is something rather than nothing, why the universe exists, why we exist....It is not necessary to invoke God to light the blue touch paper and set the universe going.*

---

[2] To get an idea of what is meant by near, the *event horizon* (the region from which no signal can escape) of a black hole of the mass of the Sun is about 3 km.

Similarly, Lawrence Krauss in *"A Universe from Nothing"* writes that

> *quantum gravity not only seems to admit that universes are created from nothing....but it could even require it.*

As we will see in chapter 9, in the first place the nothingness of which the said authors speak is not absolute nothingness and secondly, quantum gravity does not yet exist as a theory. There are simplified results that combine classical physics, quantum and gravity, the so-called semiclassical model. The *M-theory* referred to by Hawking and Mlodinow, which groups together the five fundamental superstring theories, and which we discussed in section 5.5, is a sketch of a theory in its infancy whose mathematical details are still almost unknown, and of which still you don't understand much. *Declaring that the universe can be generated from nothing based on ideas and concepts in progress is a lack of scientific honesty.*

## 6.3 Wave or Particle?

Another oddity observed in the quantum world is the dualistic behavior of waves and particles. Until the end of the nineteenth century, classical physics made a clear division between wave phenomena and those related to particles. Young's famous double slit phenomenon had shown that light behaved like a wave producing phenomena such as diffraction and interference.

In 1905, Einstein gave a description of the *photoelectric effect* that showed how light, in addition to behaving like a wave, could be considered to be made up of quanta of light, *photons*. By interacting with an atom, it can remove an electron from the orbit of an atom, and in collisions it behaves like a particle as shown in the *Compton effect*[3]. Louis de Broglie

---

[3] The Compton effect is a diffusion phenomenon that can be interpreted as a collision between a photon (intended as a particle) and an electron. It was

in his doctoral thesis of 1924, proposed that to photons is associated a wavelength, material particles (e.g., electrons) should similarly be associated with a *wave of matter* and stated that his thesis could be verified with the observation of a phenomenon of diffraction of electrons with the crystals. To test de Broglie's idea and show the wave nature of material corpuscles, Clinton Davisson and Lester Germer (and other groups) shoot electrons at reduced velocity towards a crystalline nickel target, confirming de Broglie's predictions: the electrons behaved like waves. This is one of many examples and at the same time one of the most significant of the kind of incredible observations that quantum mechanics often presents to us. So, both waves and particles have common characteristics: particles have wave behavior and waves can have particle behavior. This characteristic of nature is known as *wave-particle duality*. To solve this paradox Niels Bohr introduced the so-called *complementarity principle* which states that at the atomic and subatomic level the wave and particle nature cannot be observed during the same experiment[4]. Returning to Young's experiment, Einstein had revived Newton's corpuscular theory of light. Young, with his experiment, had apparently proved that Newton's ideas that light was made up of particles were wrong. In fact, if Young was right, Newton was not wrong. Today it is possible to repeat the double slit experiment considering a beam so weak that it emits one photon at a time and what is observed on the screen is again an interference figure. What happens is very strange because it would seem to imply an interference of photons with themselves. We will talk about this strangeness and others highlighted in the double slit experiment in a subsequent paragraph.

---

observed in 1922 by Arthur Compton and consisted of sending a beam of photons to a graphite target and observing the diffuse beam.

[4] This principle accepted for decades was put into discussion in 1991 in an experiment proposed by Partha Ghose and Grish Agarwal and carried out by other physicists. This is the double prism experiment in which the wave and corpuscular nature are observed at the same time.

## 6.4 Probability and Superposition of States

After the first formulation of quantum mechanics by Heisenberg, which proved difficult for physicists for the use of tables of numbers called matrices, Erwin Schrödinger tried to find a quantum theory following the basic idea of Newton, to formulate an authentic mechanics that could explain both the motion of bodies and the causes. Based on the known results, he attempted to obtain a formula analogous to Newton's second law, in the quantum world. Schrödinger hypothesized the existence of a function, called *wave function*, capable of containing all the information relating to the system. This equation, like Newton's second law, is a differential equation, one of those equations in the form of which physical laws are often expressed. One of the many things that Schrödinger's equation allowed to explain automatically was the quantization of energy, without introducing artificial postulates such as those used by Bohr. The wave function, in addition to solving many problems, introduced others. Until then, the equations of physics made it possible to obtain measurements with limitless precision. In quantum mechanics this is no longer possible due to the fact that Heisenberg's uncertainty principle places limits on precision in measurements. Initially it was not clear what the meaning of the wave function was. The meaning of the wave function was given by Born, who showed that the square module of the same gave probabilistic information on the position of the object studied. The certainty of classical mechanics was replaced with probability.

Some physicists found themselves uncomfortable with the introduction of probability and with the interpretation of the theory itself. If we can only measure probabilities, if the uncertainty principle places limits on measurements, if the wave-particle duality tells us that a system can behave like a wave or a particle, scientists wondered where the objectivity of physics had gone. Bohr and Heisenberg, the fathers of the so-called *Copenhagen interpretation of quantum mechanics* argued that the wave function represents everything we can know about a system, and observation and measurements were the only real thing. For example, it would make no sense to ask where the particle was and what it did before the measurement. When we observe the particle and carry out the measurement it chooses (almost like a thinking being) its position. It is said that the wave function collapses assuming a precise value. Before the collapse the particle was in the superposition of all possible states. The most critical point of the Copenhagen interpretation was for many, as mentioned, the *problem of measurement* and the *micro-macro problem*. The latter is based on the fact that the objects of the quantum world have a different behavior from macroscopic ones. The macroscopic reality is independent of the measurement, while the microscopic reality depends on the act of measurement. Since there is no physical or logical threshold that separates the micro from the macro, this problem must be explained. Erwin Schrödinger, in an attempt to ridicule the paradoxes of quantum mechanics, proposed *Schrödinger's cat paradox*.

In Schrödinger's words

> *One can even set up quite ridiculous cases. A cat is penned up in a steel chamber, along with the following device (which must be secured against direct interference by the cat): in a Geiger counter, there is a tiny bit of radioactive substance, so small that perhaps in the course of the hour, one of the atoms decays, but also, with equal probability, perhaps none; if it happens, the counter tube discharges, and through a relay releases a hammer that shatters a small flask of hydrocyanic acid. If one has left this entire system to itself for an hour, one would say that the cat still lives if meanwhile no atom has decayed. The psi-function of the entire system would express this by having in it the living and dead cat (pardon the expression) mixed or smeared out in equal parts. It is typical of these cases that an indeterminacy originally restricted to the atomic domain becomes transformed into macroscopic indeterminacy, which can then be resolved by direct observation. That prevents us from so naively accepting as valid a "blurred model" for representing reality. In itself, it would not embody anything unclear or contradictory. There is a difference between a shaky or out-of-focus photograph and a snapshot of clouds and fog banks.*

In the Copenhagen interpretation, the cat, before the measure, is in a superposition of states: alive and dead. When the box is opened (the measurement will be made) the wave function will collapse and the state will be either dead or alive.

The *superposition principle of states* has no equivalent in classical physics. For this principle, the wave function of a quantum state can represent a superposition of states and a probability is assigned to each of them. For example, when the cat is closed in the box it can be said that it has a 50% chance of being alive and 50% of being dead. The result of a measurement can only be a series of possible values, corresponding to only one of the superimposed states. This value cannot be predicted before measurement. The measurement precipitates the system into the corresponding state.

To try to solve the paradoxes related to the theory of measure and the Copenhagen interpretation, other interpretations of quantum mechanics have been introduced, such as the *many-worlds interpretation*, which we will discuss in section 8.1 or that of Bohm, just to give some examples. Despite all attempts, many of the aspects of quantum mechanics still remain not understood and will probably continue to be so because they are too far from the way in which the macroscopic world presents itself to us and because of the way in which our mind has evolved and adapted to what for us is the real.

## 6.5  The Two Slits Experiment: Teleology, Causation and God

Richard Feynman thought that the double-slit experiment *"contains the whole mystery of quantum mechanics"*. In this experiment, the strangeness of quantum mechanics is clearly highlighted. In Young's classic experiment a beam of light passes through a double slit and arrives on a screen (Figure 6.2)

Light passes through both slits. The light of one slit is combined with that of the other. If the waves arrive in phase they add up, if they arrive in phase opposition they cancel out

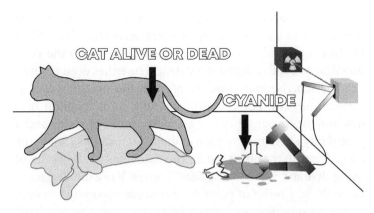

Figure 6. 1.   Schrödinger's cat experiment. Source: "Regole del gioco nella teoria dei quanti (Rules of the game in quantum theory)", Gianni Comini

**Double-slit experiment**

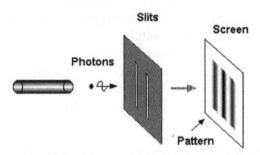

Figure 6.2.   Young's experiment

(Figure 6.3). What is observed is an *interference pattern*, i.e. a series of light areas, where the waves are in phase, and dark areas (figure 6.2) where the waves are in phase opposition, which show the wave nature of light.

If we now decrease the intensity of the beam to the point that the apparatus is crossed by only one photon at a time, what happens is that a speck is formed on the screen (the photon behaves like a particle), but if you wait, the photons reform, speck by speck, the interference pattern (figure 6.4, left). So

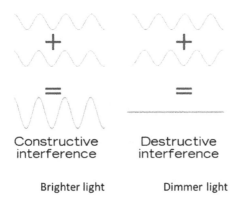

Figure 6.3.  left: waves arriving in phase and adding up. Right: waves that arrive in phase opposition and subtract

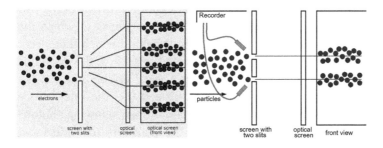

Figure 6.4.  Left: two-slit experiment with particles or photons. Right: Two-slit experiment with apparatus that determines the slit through which the photon passes. Source: "Double slit experiment decoded", Bhushan Poojary, (SSRG-IJAP) - volume 1 Issue 3 Nov-Dec 2014

the arrival of a photon is recorded as a single particle but the collective effect is to get back the interference figure. This thing is strange because it seems to imply that each photon must realize that there are two slits and that it cooperates with the others to form the interference pattern, although a photon can only pass through a slit.

In other words, one might think that the photon passes through both slits. Now let's make a small change to the experiment. Let's place an apparatus near a slit that allows us to see which slit the photon passes through. In this case, the interference pattern is not formed (Figure 6.4, right).

The experiment shows the fundamental role of the observer in the final result and also shows that light behaves both as a wave and as a particle. If we repeat the experiment with electrons the same things happen. If the two slits are open, the interference pattern will be formed. If we try to find out where an electron has passed the figure disappears. To see where the electron passes from, it is necessary to illuminate it, hit it with photons and this changes the trajectory of the electron, eliminating the interference pattern. According to the *principle of complementarity*, the photon can show either its particle nature or its wave nature. In the experiment of the two slits these natures are shown according to the experiment that is done. A question that can be asked is: when does the photon decide whether it will travel as a wave or a particle? To answer this question Wheeler thought of a variant of the two slits experiment, the *delayed choice experiment*, in which the screen consisted of Venetian blinds behind which there were two detectors each of which pointed to a slit. If the curtain is open the apparatus functions as a usual double slit, and the wave nature of the light is manifested (i.e. the interference pattern is formed) but if the curtain is open, allowing photons to pass through, one can use the detectors to understand which slit the photon has passed. In this case the corpuscular nature of light is manifested. The experimenter can then choose which nature of light to manifest: the wave or the particle one. The results of this experiment are the same as the classic slit experiment, but in this case, the trajectory of the particle, in a sense its past, is determined long after it has passed through the slits, which is the point at which it should have to "decide" whether to go through one slit and behave like a particle, or both, and behave like a wave. At the same time, the experimenter can delay the choice that the wave or particle aspect occurs until the photons have reached the curtain. At this point the question arises: when did the photon adopt the wave or particle shape, which, as we have seen, was chosen by the experimenter? How does the photon know if the curtain is open or closed? Does the photon postpone (delay) the choice to be wave or particle until the experimenter makes his choice?

The interpretation of the experiment is not trivial and there are disagreements among scientists. Some theorists argue that opening the curtain when the experiment is in progress can force a photon to retroactively decide to pass through one of the slits like a particle, when instead it had already passed as a wave and vice versa. In this way, observation has a certain relevance to the past: the choice of today's experimenter shapes the nature of the reality that was. As Paul Davies writes (in "The Goldilocks Enigma").

*That is not quite the same as explicit backward causation (which would enable the experimenter to send a signal into the past), but it does have a distinct teleological feel to it. I would describe it, in Wheeleristic terms, as "teleology without teleology".*

In a stronger way, Hawking and Mlodinow (in "The Grand Design") write.

*The universe, according to quantum physics, has no single past, or history. The fact that the past takes no definite form means that observations you make on a system in the present affect its past.*

Wheeler also thought of a cosmic version of the experiment, considering a quasar and a galaxy between us, and the quasar acting as a gravitational lens. In this case, if the light passes from both sides of the galaxy, we will observe an interference figure, while if we used a device to determine the path of the photon, this figure would not be observed. Unlike the usual delayed choice experiment, in this case the choice to follow one or both trajectories would have been made billions of years ago, before the Earth existed: our observation would influence the choice. The delayed choice experiment was carried out using both double slit and interferometers by Caroll Alley at the University of Maryland, and a *delayed choice quantum cancellation experiment* was carried out by Kim et al in 2000 which allows for a 50% chance to verify where the photon passed 8 nanoseconds after it collided with the screen.

As seen, several scientists cite these types of experiments as an example of *backward causation*, that is, that the cause precedes the effect, and that the observer determines reality. A careful analysis of these experiments has led several other scientists to argue that this is incorrect. Other scientists such as Bruckner's group in Vienna and Chiribella's in Hong Kong have shown that the causal structure of everyday life may not work in quantum mechanics.

They showed that random relationships can be placed in superposition states in which an event A influences an event B but also B influences A. Even before Bruckner and Chiribella, in the 1940s Wheeler and Feynman proposed a theory in which electromagnetic and electrodynamic interactions can travel into the future and into the past. In other fields, such as quantum cosmology Gell-Mann and Hartle and Hawking proposed backward causation theories. However, none of these theories has ever been experimentally verified. Now, one of the arguments used to prove the existence of God, starting from Plato to Aristotle, Thomas Aquinas, and Kant is based on the causal chain: everything has a cause and the first cause is identified with God. Now if the principle of causality no longer works, the argument of the first cause is shattered, and with it God existence. If determinism and causality are violated, as we have seen, particles and even universes can appear in a sudden and unpredictable way. The universe does not need a first cause. Wheeler based on his delayed choice experiment proposed the possibility for observers of today and the future to forge the nature of physical reality in the past, even the distant past in which there were no observers. For Wheeler, observers are participants in forging reality. For him, the cosmos generated life, from this the mind that played a creative role in the Universe was born. Living beings using quantum mechanics through backward causation or other principles not yet known, could interrogate nature to obtain information and this allows for the forging of reality even in the distant past. In other words, the universe is created by the observer-participants in a sort of cycle of existence. These ideas are close to some ideas of Eastern philosophy. As F. Capra wrote in "The Tao of Physics"

*The idea of "participation instead of observation" has been formulated in modern physics only recently , but it is an idea which is well known to any student of mysticism. Mystical knowledge can never be obtained just by observation, but only by full participation with one's whole being. The notion of the participator is crucial to the Eastern world vie, and the Easter mystics have pushed this notion to the extreme, to a point where the observer and observed, subject and object, are not only inseparable but also become indistinguishable*

From the previous arguments, can we conclude that quantum physics denies the existence of God? The answer is no, for several reasons. The backward causation referred to in Wheeler's thought experiment is not accepted by many physicists and even if it were correct there is a huge leap between the *delayed choice experiment* dealing with photons to the idea that the Universe is created by observer-participant. Experiments dealing with the causality principle are still in their infancy. It takes time and other experiments to understand its true meaning. Finally, as already mentioned and as we will see in chapter 9, creating a universe from nothing (i.e. absence of energy, space, time, physical laws) is not contemplated in current physics.

## 6.6 Feynman and the Sum Over All Paths

The two-slit experiment can be used to describe another formulation of quantum mechanics proposed by Richard Feynman. When we shoot an electron at the device, it should go through the left or right slit. Well, Feynman denied this intuitive idea and claimed that the electron actually goes through both slits before reaching the screen. To be more precise, according to Feynman, the electron not only passes through both slits, but it travels all possible trajectories between the point from which it was shot and the screen where it arrives, simultaneously. Not just the trajectories close to the fissures, but any trajectory, even a trajectory leading to Mars and back. The electron, like a truffle dog, sniffs all the trajectories between the starting point and the arrival point, so it knows how many slits there are and which of the slits are open. Then the electron passes from the first slit and from the second and the interaction of these trajectories give rise to interference. Each trajectory is associated with a number, called *phase*, which gives information if the wave is at its maximum, minimum or in an intermediate position. When we add up the waves relative to all the trajectories we find the amplitude of probability that the particle goes from a point A to a point B. So doing the sum on all the paths we get the same results that gives the solution of the equation by Schrödinger. It is not necessary to associate a probability wave with the electron.

If the method is applied to a macroscopic object, the phases of the trajectories close to the Newtonian path reinforce each other, while the phases of the trajectories further away from

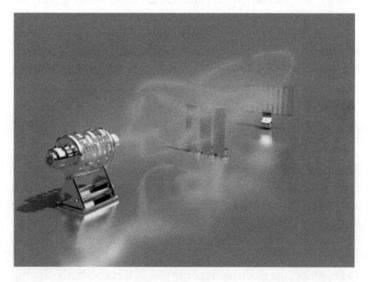

Figure 6.5. Explanation of the two-slit experiment in Feynman's formulation of quantum mechanics. Source: S. Hawking, Leonard Mlodinow, "The Grand Design"

this path cancel each other out. The remaining trajectory is that described by Newton's laws. Feynman's method can also be applied to a system of various particles or to the "system" of the universe. Although Feynman's approach is reduced to classical mechanics in the case of macroscopic objects, there is always a very small probability that the macroscopic world will have a quantum behavior, if one has the patience to wait long enough. For example, if we observe the Moon, it follows its path in orbit around the Earth, over the centuries and millennia. If absurdly we could observe the motion of the Moon for an infinite time (if our solar system and the universe had an infinite life) it could happen to see it come out of its orbit (as in the serial *Space 1999*) take a walk to another planet and then another. Since quantum mechanics is governed by probability, waiting long enough for the possible to come true. Although quantum mechanics does not directly manifest itself in our life as being macroscopic, our existence depends on it. Reality, however solid it appears to us, has at its basis the quantum structure that holds reality in place. For example, without the *tunnel effect* mentioned in section 4.1, our Sun could not shine and we would not be here. For nuclear reactions to occur in the Sun, the protons must fuse to form helium. When two protons approach each other the electromagnetic force (the Coulomb barrier) grows and they do not collide, but come back, in most cases. Thanks to the tunnel effect, every now and then, two protons overcome the electromagnetic force and in some cases they can merge.

Fusion occurs only in a few cases (even when the protons have passed the Coulomb barrier) because even if the two protons overcome the Coulomb repulsion thanks to the tunnel effect, they immediately detach or decay into neutrons. However, in about ten billion years, a proton in the nucleus is successfully involved in a nuclear fusion cycle. The number of protons in the sun is very large and every second about $3.4 \times 10^{38}$ protons are transformed into helium. To conclude, I would like to mention that electronic devices such as computers, televisions, etc., work thanks to quantum mechanics.

## 6.7 Entanglement and Non-locality: spooky Actions at a Distance

At the end of the 20s of the last century, the main results of quantum mechanics seemed well defined and firm, so much so that in the Solvay congress of 1927, Born and Heisenberg said

> *we consider quantum mechanics to be a closed theory, whose fundamental physical and mathematical assumptions are no longer susceptible to change*

A few years later, in 1935, an article was published that challenged the beliefs of complete and solid quantum mechanics. The article, entitled *Can quantum-mechanical description of physical reality be considered complete?*, published by Albert Einstein, Boris Podolsky and Nathan Rosen (hence the name: EPR paper) in Physical Review attacked the idea that quantum mechanics gave a unique and complete description of reality. The authors, starting from some hypotheses such as *realism*[5] (realism means that all the measurements carried out on "real" objects reveal pre-existing and independent physical properties with respect to the observation itself), the *locality*[6], (i.e. that distant objects cannot have an instantaneous influence on the one on the other), and *completeness*, came to show that there is a contradiction in the simultaneous assumption of realism, the *principle of locality and the completeness* of quantum mechanics. From this they deduced that quantum mechanics is incomplete. Let's see how this conclusion is reached. Suppose we collide an electron and a positron which annihilating will generate two photons, one A and the other B. The electron and the positron have spin zero

---

[5] If, without disturbing a physical system in any way, one is able to predict with certainty the value of a physical quantity, then there is an *element of physical reality* associated with this quantity.

[6] If a system A is physically separate from a system B, even though it has interacted with A in the past, no physical action on A can affect the elements of reality in B.

and since the photons have spin 1, it must result that if one of them has value +1 the other must have –1. Similarly to the case of Schrödinger's cat, each photon is in a superposition of states +1 and –1. If we make a measurement and find that photon A has spin +1, we understand that the other has spin –1, since the spin must be zero. Now suppose we insert each photon in a box and send photon B to the other side of the galaxy. We measure A's spin which is +1, and immediately know that B will have spin –1. The question that arises is: how does B know that its spin must be –1? How is information transmitted thousands of light years away instantly? According to the locality principle, the two photons should be independent. The experiment tells us that information is transmitted at superluminal speed, through some *spooky action at a distance*, as Einstein said.

According to him, quantum mechanics was incomplete and the two particles were correlated from the beginning through *hidden variables*. It was necessary to assume the existence of hidden variables that would provide the missing information about the system. In other words, Einstein and collaborators argued that there should be a theory, called the *theory of hidden variables*, of which quantum mechanics is an approximation. This theory would contain variables that take into account all the *physical elements of reality* (observable) that generate the effects that quantum mechanics can predict only at a probabilistic level.

In reality, quantum mechanics violates the principle of locality, but not relativity. This is because the two photon system, even if they are in opposite parts of the Universe, constitute a single system regulated by a single wave function. When measuring, the wave function instantly assumes a state, spin +1 for A and –1 for B. There is no signal transmission and therefore relativity is not violated. In 1964, the thought experiment, namely the EPR experiment, was experimentally tested. With his inequalities Bell tested whether or not there were hidden variables. Since that experiment all the various other experiments (e.g., that of Aspect) have confirmed the existence of a quantum correlation of a non-local type, and that two interacting particles sharing the same wave function (entangled particles, i.e. correlated) can "communicate" even at superluminal speeds without violating relativity. Ultimately the *local realism*[7] is not correct and furthermore two correlated objects continue to be a single system even if they are located at very large distances in space-time. Reality is entangled and not separable into the individual components. Einstein in his ultimate attempt to destroy quantum mechanics strengthened it and created a new field of research. *Quantum entanglement* is a phenomenon that has led to a multitude of discoveries and opened new fields of research such as *quantum cryptography* and *teleportation*.

In conclusion, does quantum mechanics deny God? As we have seen, if the principle of causality were truly violated in the microscopic world, the concept of the first cause would be lost and we could even say that it is the universe that created God and not vice versa. This conclusion is limited by the fact that in reality we are not certain that causality is violated in the microscopic world, and we do not fully understand quantum mechanics. Repeating the words of Feynman "*I think I can say with certainty that nobody understands quantum mechanics*".

We have not yet been able to understand the scale at which things do not behave according to the rules of everyday life and begin to follow the bizarre laws of quantum mechanics. A point of view similar to that of Feynman comes to us from physicist and philosopher Bernard d'Espagnat and by Bell himself. d'Espagnat's studies on quantum mechanics, his experiments on Bell's inequality and elementary particles, his philosophical studies led him to see the physical world as a mere appearance, a veil over a much larger reality. According to d'Espagnat, science can help us explain the nature of the universe to a certain extent. In his words:

> *Quantum mechanics introduced another point of view, which consists essentially that the aim of science is not to describe*

---

[7] The principle of realism plus that of locality are called the local realism principle.

*ultimate reality as it really is. Rather, it is to make account of reality as it appears to us, accounting for the limitations of our own mind and our own sensibilities. It's not that science will explain the ultimate reality of certain objects or events. Rather, it is that the concepts we use, such as space, time, causality, and so on, ... are not applicable to ultimate reality.*

Bell himself tried to understand the profound truths of quantum mechanics and their reactions to reality. Like d'Espagnat he believed that the reality behind quantum mechanics was beyond human understanding.

Apart our limits of understanding quantum mechanics, God is not subject to the laws of nature and does not have to reduce himself to the microscopic level in order to create an initially microscopic universe. As for the discourse of the origin ex-nihilo of the universe, as has been said several times, we do not have a complete theory of quantum gravity that allows us to take a closer look at this problem. Even if we had it, it could perhaps tell us, as we will discuss in chapter 9, how an entity containing no space and time could generate a universe, but two problems would remain: 1. the nothingness from which the universe is created is not the absolute nothing and 2. the problem remains of who gave rise to physical laws. In other words, quantum mechanics doesn't have much to say about God.

## Summary: Key Notes

- We have seen that quantum mechanics is a theory that shows many oddities and that what happens in the microscopic world is extremely non-intuitive. The uncertainty does not allow us to know the trajectory of a particle, it limits the knowledge on its position and speed and at the same time generates a world full of quantum, energetic fluctuations, which make it possible the appearance from the vacuum of particles that then disappear from where they came from. If we take into account the effects of quantum mechanics on the gravitational field, using approximate methods, we see that the nature of black holes is changed, they are no longer so black but emit radiation and sooner or later they will disappear in a pyrotechnic explosion. They can be created and destroyed, like particles, universes, although not out of absolute nothing.

- The microscopic world is not as solid as the macroscopic one appears to us, even the particles behave like waves.
- Quantum mechanics describes a non-deterministic world in which probability reigns supreme, a world in which, when not observed, objects are in a superposition of states and when we make an observation this disturbs the systems under study which give a manifestation of oneself according to how we observe them.
- Quantum mechanics even seems to dismantle one of the cornerstones of our world view: the principle of causality. As Aczel writes in *Why science does not disprove God* "*in the quantum world you could not tell if a match thrown on the ground caused a forest fire or if the forest fire caused the match to light!*"
- In some speculations based on quantum mechanics, observers could be participants in evolution and give rise to the universe.
- Another profound oddity that quantum mechanics offers us is a universe in which very distant objects can have instant "communication". The wave function that describes entangled objects is unique and can extend throughout the Universe. Indeed the universe itself, at least in the early days, has its own wave function that makes it similar to any particle.
- Quantum mechanics as, discussed in the final part of the chapter, doesn't have much to say about God.

# CHAPTER 7

# THE ANTHROPIC PRINCIPLE

*The more I examine the universe*
*and the details of its architecture,*
*the more evidence I find*
*that the universe in some sense must*
*have known we were coming*

— F. Dyson

## 7.1 The Control Panel of the Universe

Often physicists, starting from the twentieth century, have asked themselves the question of why the forces present in the Universe and in general the physical constants, had the value we measure. Mysterious coincidences suggest that these values do not have a random origin and this brings with it several questions, the first of which is: were the values of the constants chosen so that the Universe was populated by being intelligent? More generally: why are the laws of physics the ones we observe? Could they be different? The purpose of physics and science should be to discover the laws and study them. The questions we asked above become more part of metaphysics, philosophy, or religion than physics. However, there is no global agreement on this point. The theory that describes the forces and particles within our Universe, the so-called standard model of particles, is governed by 19 parameters, or 26 if it is extended to consider massive neutrinos. It is as if our Universe has a control panel consisting of 19 (or 26) knobs, varying which the characteristics of the same would vary. By turning a few of these knobs a little, we would obtain a Universe in which life could not exist. As we will see in a moment, our Universe is finely tuned, as discussed by Fred

Hoyle in his *Intelligent Universe*, or Martin Reese in *The Six Numbers of the Universe*, among others. That is, small changes in the fundamental constants would change everything and life would no longer be possible. One might wonder if the positions of the knobs were chosen randomly, and if the result of having a Universe containing intelligent life is the result of chance, or if there is a reason why the constants have the values they have, and that a deeper and more complete theory is needed to explain what we observe.

Unfortunately we do not have a theory explaining the values of the parameters and for this a surrogate method has been introduced which justifies the observed values. In this context, one of the most popular theories is the *anthropic principle*, which states that scientific observations in the physical-cosmological field are linked to our existence as observers. The principle tries to explain the characteristics of our Universe on the basis of the previous concept. In *The Emperor New Mind*, Roger Penrose describes the weak version of the anthropic principle in the following way.

> *The argument can be used to explain why the conditions happen to be just right for the existence of (intelligent) life on the Earth at the present time. For if they were not just right, then we should not have found ourselves to be here now, but somewhere else, at some other appropriate time. This principle was used very effectively by Brandon Carter and Robert Dicke to resolve an issue that had puzzled physicists for a good many years. The issue concerned various striking numerical relations that are observed to hold between the physical constants ... A puzzling aspect of this was that some of the relations hold only at the present epoch in the Earth's history, so we appear, co-incidentally, to be living at a very special time (give or take a few million years!). This was later explained, by Carter and Dicke, by the fact that this epoch coincided with the lifetime of what are called main-sequence stars, such as the Sun. At any other epoch, the argument ran, there would be no intelligent life around to measure the physical constants in question — so the coincidence had to hold, simply because there would be*

*intelligent life around only at the particular time that the coin-cidence did hold!*

As you can see, this principle does not give us scientific information, plus it is a kind of tautology.

This principle has been used in some cases, to determine the range in which some constants could be found, for example the value of the cosmological constant. Returning to the values of the constants or parameters of the standard model, as mentioned, one might wonder why they are so well tuned to allow intelligent life. Is this a case, albeit unlikely, or are there deeper reasons? To see how unlikely these parameters are likely to have the value they do, we can try an experiment, change their value, and see what happens.

If the nuclear force were a few percent greater than it is, the helium-2 nucleus (unstable isotope of helium) would be stable. According to Paul Davies, helium instead of generating deuterium and helium would form helium-2 nuclei, changing stellar physics and the presence of life on Earth.

The weak force produces the transformation of protons into neutrons, part of the reactions that make the Sun shine. Changes to its intensity would again lead to change in stellar physics and the existence of life on Earth. If the efficiency of nuclear reactions in the nucleus of stars were slightly higher, the hydrogen present at the beginning of the Universe would have turned into helium and water could not have existed. On the contrary, if the efficiency were lower, the central reactions would not have taken place, giving rise to a universe made only of hydrogen. In the particular case of reactions in stars, there is actually no real fine-tuning, as the variations in efficiency should be of the order of 20%.

Continuing in our excursus, small changes in the gravitational constant would modify the planetary orbits and influence the reactions in the stars, their life cycle, their size, their mass limit before they turn into black holes. If gravity had been stronger, the stars would have had a shorter life cycle, as more energy would have been required to balance the greater weight of the star. The stars would have been smaller, with a shorter life cycle providing less time for the development of life.

Again, this would lead to catastrophic effects on life. Furthermore, the formation of large-scale structures depends on the intensity of the gravitational force. A stronger gravity would generate a completely different Universe, and much greater values of gravity would have caused the cosmos to collapse very quickly, not allowing the formation of galaxies, stars and therefore planets on which life could be born. If the number of spatial dimensions were different from 3, the gravitational force would no longer decrease with the square of the distance and there would be problems similar to the one previously indicated. If in the early stages of the Universe the mass density had been slightly greater than a density called *critical density*, the Universe would have expanded quickly and forever without life being formed. On the contrary, if it had been greater, the Universe would have collapsed immediately. One second after the Big Bang, the ratio between the density and the critical one, called the *density parameter* $\Omega$, could not differ from 1 by a factor of $10^{15}$ (one million billion). If today the density of the Universe differed by less than 1% from the critical one, in the early Universe the deviation should be less than one part in $10^{61}$. This problem, as already seen, is called the *flatness problem*. This fine-tuning problem has been addressed, together with others, as already seen, by the theory of *cosmic inflation*.

Another very interesting aspect is the process of formation of the element on which life on Earth is based, carbon-12 ($^{12}C$). In order to have abundant quantities of it, the process of formation of this element in the stars must be *"finely tuned"*[1]. Furthermore, for carbon to exist in sufficient

---

[1] This element cannot be formed in the primordial phases of the universe, but is formed in the stars. The formation process is called 3 $\alpha$, where $\alpha$ indicates a helium nucleus ($^4He$). In the process, two $\alpha$ particles fuse to form a beryllium-8 ($^8Be$) nucleus which is unstable. However, during the reaction small quantities of beryllium-8 are formed which colliding with an $\alpha$ particle give rise to an excited state of carbon-12. The chances of this reaction are very small. Fortunately, beryllium-8 has almost the same energy as two $\alpha$ particles, and furthermore the reaction beryllium-8 + $\alpha$ particle ($^8Be$ + $^4He$) has the same energy level as the excited state of carbon-12. Such "resonances" increase the likelihood that an incident $\alpha$ particle will combine

quantities, there must be another process that blocks its transmutation into oxygen, a process that does indeed exist. As another example we can consider the difference in mass between protons and neutrons. Had these been slightly heavier than they are, the neutron-proton ratio would have been altered resulting in more He-4 production and less hydrogen. There would not have been enough hydrogen to trigger nuclear reactions in the primordial stars and the Universe would have remained dark, the heavy elements would not have formed inside the stars, neither the planets would have formed nor we would have been born. In the book already cited, *The Six Numbers of the Universe*, Martin Reese describes in detail how making slight changes to 6 quantities (1. ratio of the electric and gravitational force; 2. the intensity of the nuclear force; 3. the fine tuning of the "rate" of cosmic expansion; 4. the cosmological constant and dark energy; 5. The anisotropies of the CMB; 6. The existence of only 3 extended spatial dimensions), the Universe would not be as it is. Then there is the curious case of the fine structure constant, very close to 1/137 which has caused generations of physicists to be damned in an attempt to explain it. Richard Feynman wrote

*It's one of the greatest damn mysteries of physics: a magic number that comes to us with no understanding by man. You might say the "hand of God" wrote that number, and "we don't know how He pushed his pencil." We know what kind of a dance to do experimentally to measure this number very accurately, but we don't know what kind of dance to do on the computer to make this number come out, without putting it in secretly!*

---

with beryllium-8, forming carbon-12. The formation of carbon-12, based on the idea that an undiscovered excited level was present in it, consisting of a resonant energy with the combined energy of the two starting nuclei, is due to Fred Hoyle. Put simply, the formation of carbon-12 requires considerable "luck". The discovery of the said "resonance" was considered by the proponents of the anthropic principle one of the arguments in support of their idea, because it is linked to the appearance of life.

None of the attempts to explain the values of the constants have been successful. As we will see in the next section, Stephen Weinberg managed, in the case of the cosmological constant, to give a correct range in which it could be found, before it was measured.

The most extreme case of fine-tuning, linked to entropy, is the one described by Roger Penrose. In *The Emperor's new mind* and *The Road to Reality*, Penrose, ask the question of how special was the big bang. Penrose considers the phase space[2] of the entire Universe. Each cell in this phase space represents a way in which the Universe could have originated. He goes on to calculate the volume, E, of the phase space of the Universe, which in Penrose's calculation is equal to $10^{10^{123}}$. Let's compare this value to that of the volume N of the cell for the current entropy and to the volume B of the cell for entropy when the Big Bang occurred. Penrose finds B: N: E $= 10^{10^{88}}$: $10^{10^{101}}$: $10^{10^{123}}$. So each B and N constitute one part in $10^{10^{123}}$ of the total volume. So thinking in terms of phase space, the precision required for a Big Bang like that of our Universe is at least 1 in $10^{10^{123}}$. This is obviously an infinitesimally small region and if the creator wants to create a universe like ours he must locate that region.

In the Emperor's new mind Penrose writes

*Try to imagine the phase space...of the entire universe! Each point in this phase space represents a different possible way that the universe might have started off. We are to picture the Creator, armed with a `pin' which is to be placed at some point in the phase space..... Each different positioning of the pin provides a different universe. Now the accuracy that is needed for the Creator's aim depends upon the entropy of the universe that is thereby created. It would be relatively `easy' to produce a high entropy universe, since then there would be a large volume of the phase space available for the pin to*

---

[2] In classical mechanics the phase space is represents all the positions and speeds of each point. In the theory of dynamic systems, the phase space is the space whose points uniquely represent all and only the possible states of the system.

*hit. ....But in order to start off the universe in state of low entropy-so that there will indeed be a second law of thermo-dynamics-the Creator must aim for a much tinier volume of the phase space. How tiny would this region be, in order that a universe closely resembling the one in which we actually live would be the result?*

*.......... we are considering a closed universe so eventually it should recollapse; and it is not unreasonable to estimate the entropy of the final crunch by using the Bekenstein-Hawking formula as though the whole universe had formed a black hole. This gives an entropy per baryon of $10^{43}$, and the ab-solutely stupendous total, for the entire big crunch would be $10^{123}$.*

*This figure will give us an estimate of the total phase-space volume V available to the Creator, since this entropy should represent the logarithm of the volume of the (easily) largest compartment. Since $10^{123}$ is the logarithm of the volume, the volume must be the exponential of $10^{123}$, i.e.*

$$V = 10^{10^{123}}.$$

*in natural units!*

If the entire Universe is not needed to have intelligent life, the previous request is lowered to 1 in $10^{10^{117}}$. These numbers indicate how special the conditions that gave rise to our Universe were. This fine-tuning is by far the most significant. Especially for this fine-tuning it is not surprising what Paul Davies writes in "*The Intelligent Cosmos*":

*It seems as though somebody has fine-tuned nature's num-ber to make the Universe... The impression of design is over-whelming*

One could continue this argument with the other fundamental constants and with the 19 (or 26) parameters of the *standard model of particles*. The first thing that could come to mind is that therefore there is an intelligent project, perhaps behind which there is a Creator. Indeed, if there was only one Universe, it would be difficult not to accept this conclusion. In the last years, however, physicists seem to have found a solution. As we will see in chapter 8, there could be an infinity of Universes (the *multiverse*) all with different constants and therefore among all the infinite combinations of these parameters, coincidentally, there would also be the right one. This is similar to our planet. Also in this case, there are a lot of combinations (distance of the Earth from the Sun, etc.) that must have precise values for life to be formed on Earth. It is like the fairy tale of *Goldilocks and the three bears*, the porridge must not be too hot or too cold. However, in 1995 the first exoplanets were discovered and today it is thought that there are billions of them just in our galaxy. In some of those billions there will be the right conditions for life to be formed.

## 7.2 The Cosmological Constant and Life in Our Universe

Two years after the publication of his treatise on the Theory of General Relativity, in 1917, Einstein applied it to the Universe and found results that contradicted his prejudices and those of his time: that is, the static nature of the Universe. He found that his equations predicted an expanding or contracting Universe. Demonstrating, in that case, little faith in his equations, and following the generalized prejudice that the Universe was static, he introduced a constant in his equations, the *cosmological constant* $\Lambda$, which acting repulsively countered the gravitational attraction and caused Universe could remain static.

In 1922, the Russian Aleksander Friedman showed that general relativity predicted an endlessly expanding universe, or an expanding universe followed by a collapse. This was confirmed by the Jesuit priest, George Lemaitre, and by Edwin Hubble, with observations, in 1929. This led Einstein to exclude the cosmological constant from his equations. In the late 1990s, the *Supernova Cosmology Project* and the *High-Z Supernova Search Team* dedicated themselves to search for Type

Ia Supernovae to measure the expansion rate of the Universe. The importance of Supernovae Ia is that they are standard candles, reference stars for which the *absolute magnitude* or *intrinsic brightness* can be determined. From the intrinsic luminosity and the apparent luminosity, that is the observed luminosity, it is possible to trace the distance. Supernovae Ia originated from the explosion of white carbon-oxygen dwarfs, devoid of hydrogen. Low-rotation white dwarfs have an upper limit for their mass called the *Chandrasekhar limit*, equivalent to 1.44 solar masses. If the white dwarf is in a binary system, its mass can increase when the mass of the companion falls on it. When the mass of the white dwarf approaches the Chandrasekhar limit, the temperature in its core can reach the values necessary for the fusion of carbon. Within seconds from the start of the merger, much of the star's mass is subjected to a thermonuclear reaction that releases an enormous amount of energy capable of producing a violent explosion. In the explosion of type Ia supernovae, the brightness grows very rapidly and reaches an intrinsic brightness equal to that of a few billion suns. Furthermore, the intrinsic brightness is very similar in all explosions of this type due to the uniformity of the masses of the exploding dwarfs.

A decay of brightness follows and after a few hundred days most of the SnIa disappear in the glow of the host galaxy. Therefore, the mass of the white dwarfs at the moment of the explosion is the same in all of them and the physics of the explosion that gives rise to the supernova is similar in all white dwarfs. Consequently, the energy released, the characteristics of the explosion and those of the supernova phenomenon are very similar in different supernovae which thus constitute standard candles. The result of the studies was that the Universe expands in an accelerated manner. The astronomers were taken by surprise. The acceleration was explained in terms of the cosmological constant, which was first introduced by Einstein and then eliminated after the Hubble observations. Nobody knew what kind of process could give rise to effects such as those of a cosmological constant having a small but not zero value. The standard model predicts that there is energy in a vacuum. Calculating this energy with quantum mechanics and comparing it with the observed value we find that the theoretical value is $10^{120}$ greater than the observed one. The problem still remains today the most disastrous prediction of theoretical physics. The value of the cosmological constant is a case of cosmic coincidence, because if it had been equal to the value predicted by the theory, the Universe would have expanded very quickly without forming structures and therefore without giving rise to life. In other words, the value of the cosmological constant is one of the few compatible with life. Several authors have tried to predict the existence of dark energy and estimate the value of the cosmological constant without success. Stephen Weinberg (famous for being together with Abdus Salam and Sheldon Glashow the architect of the electroweak theory and for his contributions to the construction of the standard model. For these results he obtained the Nobel Prize in 1979) succeeded. In a well-known article in 1987, he was able to establish the range of values in which the cosmological constant could be found. To do this he used an often criticized method, the *anthropic principle*. Weinberg's ideas were that our existence conditions the Universe, that the cosmological constant had different values in different spatial regions. One can determine the value compatible with our existence. Weinberg excluded places with cosmological constant too large or too small because in those regions the structures that support life would be suppressed. He also assumed that $\Lambda$ was non-zero, given the very low probability that this would happen. In other words, Weinberg made predictions on the values of the cosmological constant based on the idea that its values should be compatible with the fact that we exist. In another 1989 paper Weinberg calculated the maximum value of the vacuum energy compatible with the existence of observers. Similar to his 1987 work, he came to the conclusion that the energy density of the vacuum must be small enough not to prevent the formation of large-scale structures. If dark energy had had a negative value, the universe would have collapsed and if the size of the energy had been very large, the universe would have expanded so rapidly that it did not form structures, stars and planets and life. Based on these arguments, Weinberg established a range of acceptable values for the dark energy density $\rho_\Lambda$ between 10 and 100 times that associated with matter, $\rho_m$, being $\rho_m$ the density of ordinary and dark matter. Weinberg's theory was perfected in 1995 by Alexander Vilenkin, adding to Weinberg's assumptions the idea that the cosmological constant favored the maintenance of the maximum amount of matter in galaxies. He found a value for the cosmological constant at most ten times that of the density of matter. For values about ten times greater than those observed, the Universe would expand too fast for galaxies to form, and this would preclude the existence of life. We can therefore imagine what would happen if the cosmological constant were $10^{120}$ times greater than the observed value. It must be remembered that "*although the use of the cosmological principle allows us to find a range for the values of the cosmological constant, it does not explain why this is so, except from the tautology "we have that range of values only because we are here to observe it*".

So if the cosmological principle does not have great predictive power, it assumes predictive power if there is a multitude of universes with different physical characteristics. The value of dark energy is obtained from the sum of the various contributions of quantum fields. There are enormous contributions, both positive and negative, to dark energy and this usually leads to its excessively large value. So in most universes the magnitude of the energy will be too large to allow life to appear. In a small number of them these contributions will offsct cach othcr so as to fit within the limit found by Weinberg and life will be possible. To make life on Earth possible, it is not enough that the cosmological constant has certain values, but the fundamental constants, the characteristics of the forces must have particular values. Small variations of them would not produce the Universe we see. As mentioned previously, an example that better makes us understand why the anthropic principle assumes a certain importance in the case that it is applied to a multitude of physical systems with different characteristics is that of the exoplanets. If only our planetary system existed in the universe, it would be difficult to explain why it has all the characteristics to host life. This would lead us to think that "someone" has maneuvered the system so that it respects the characteristics necessary for birth, and for the evolution of life. After 1995, we know that in our galaxy alone there are billions of planetary systems, each different from the other. Some with stars bigger than the Sun and planets bigger than ours. There will be a myriad of combinations of parameters. Among the various statistical combinations there are those that make the existence of life on Earth possible. There are billions of planets on which life does not exist and probably a handful on which it does. Since we exist, we must be in one of these rare planets suitable for life. For life to exist in the universe, it is necessary that $\Lambda$ and the parameters of the standard model have particular values. In short, the Universe is so suitable for life either because there was a great architect who thought of everything down to the smallest detail or because there are a huge number of universes. That is, there is a multiverse and the Universe is suitable for life simply by a selection effect. A last possibility is that the Universe is so suitable for life simply by chance.

## 7.3 The Anthropic Principles

We have seen that the anthropic principle, although not a scientific theory, helps us to resolve paradoxes characterizing our Universe. To be precise, there are different forms of the anthropic principle. The first formulation is due to Brandon Carter in 1973. The phrase anthropic principle appeared for the first time in a contribution by Brandon Carter in a Symposium held in Krakow in honor of Copernicus' 500th birthday, in 1973. The term anthropic principle was pronounced in reaction to the term Copernican principle, which asserts that man does not occupy a privileged position in the Universe. As Carter said *"although our situation is not central it is inevitably privileged"*. In particular, Carter was against using the Copernican principle to justify the *perfect cosmological principle* (the concept underlying the Theory of the Steady

State) that is, the idea that the Universe is homogeneous in space and time, and consequently immutable and eternal.

In 1965 it was shown that this theory was wrong and that the Universe changes over time. At that time, most astronomers believed that the Universe was homogeneous in space and time and the Big Bang was not considered a serious theory because it put humanity in a privileged situation. While the conditions of the Universe have been adverse in most of its history, humanity existed precisely in a favorable time. This coincidence was not well received, while for Carter there was no coincidence. According to him, we are in a random region among regions that allow our life, not in a random region among all possible ones. Carter formulated two forms of the anthropic principle. The weak anthropic principle and the strong anthropic principle. The first says

> We must be prepared to take account of the fact that our location in the universe is necessarily privileged to the extent of being compatible with our existence as observers,

while the strong one

> The universe (and consequently the fundamental parameters that characterize it) must be such as to allow the creation of observers within it at a given stage [of its existence].

If the "must" is to be understood as a necessity, given that we know we exist, the *strong anthropic principle* would be a tautology, while if the "must" indicates that something forces the Universe to generate observers, we are facing an unscientific position. The major objections to the anthropic principle generally refer to the latter interpretation of the strong anthropic principle, popularized by Frank Tipler and John D. Barrow, in the book *The cosmological anthropic principle*. The authors argued that the laws of the Universe must be made in such a way as to allow life, which implies that the cause of the laws of the Universe is life, reintroducing the Aristotelian concept of *final cause* into science. This reinterpretation of the anthropic principle has aroused controversy. The two authors provided new formulations of the principle. Their version of the weak anthropic principle is

> *The observed values of all physical and cosmological quantities are not equally probable but are limited by the requirement that there are places where carbon-based life can evolve and by the requirement that the universe is old enough to have already allowed it.*

The strong anthropic principle is formulated like this

> *The Universe must have those properties which allow life to develop within it at some stage in its history.*

Another form of the strong anthropic principle is the one proposed by John Archibald Wheeler, the so-called *participatory anthropic principle*. This variant of the anthropic principle is linked to the *Copenhagen interpretation of quantum mechanics* and to the backward causation of the *delayed choice experiment*, already seen in section 6.5. While in classical physics the state of a particle is specified by its position and speed, in quantum mechanics the state of a particle or of a generic system is represented by the wave function, which evolves with time, and whose square gives the probability of finding the system in a certain state. In the Copenhagen interpretation, the measurement discontinuously disturbs the state of the system and happens the so-called *collapse of the wave function*, following which the quantity being measured takes on the measured value. In this formulation, observation and the observer become protagonists of the evolution of physical systems, to the point that one cannot assume the existence of a certain reality without an observer who measures it. Regarding this aspect, Einstein once ironically asked Abraham Pais *"Are you really convinced that the Moon only exists if you look at it?"*

In the Copenhagen interpretation of quantum mechanics the only real thing are the results of the measurements and this denies the reality of the wave function, and consequently denies the existence of a single reality when a measurement is not made. More precisely, the Copenhagen interpretation does not pronounce on external reality when it is not observed and this leads us to think that it is legitimate that reality does not exist if it is not observed. Wheeler suggested that if we take the Copenhagen interpretation seriously we come to the conclusion that unless a phenomenon is observed it cannot be affirmed. In other words, observers are needed to give meaning to the Universe. Tipler and Barrow took Wheeler's idea further by concluding that the universe does not exist if there are no observers. As already seen, Wheeler came to think of a sort of cycle in which the universe created the observer-participants, which gave rise to the mind and this through quantum mechanics was able to influence the distant past of the universe. In reality, a more in-depth examination of the Copenhagen interpretation says that before measurement, reality exists as a superposition of states. To the extent the superposition of states collapses into only one. In terms of observers and the universe, the presence of observers forces the universe to choose a state, but it does not generate its existence. Furthermore, in observation, a system of the microcosm is related to one of the macrocosm that does not necessarily have to be conscious. Nowadays, ultimately the participatory anthropic principle, and in general, the anthropic principles in versions of final cause are considered unacceptable.

## 7.4 The Anthropic Principle does not Work if there is no Multiverse

As already mentioned, the predictive potential of the anthropic principle depends on the existence of a multiverse in which the physical laws are variable from universe to universe. If the multiverse did not exist, *the anthropic principle would be reduced to a mere tautology.* In this sense, the validity of the anthropic principle is linked to a mechanism that generates the multiverse, such as chaotic inflation or string theory. There are many discussions on the validity of the anthropic principle. A fairly well-known one is that of Leonard Susskind and Lee Smolin. Susskind is a supporter of the anthropic principle while Smolin claims that it is unscientific. Part of the debate between the two is based on determining the range of values in which the cosmological constant would be found using the anthropic principle. From Smolin's point of view, Weinberg's argument would be based on four points, combining the relationship between the values of the cosmological constant, the formation of galaxies and the existence of observers. More precisely, Weinberg would have assumed that a too large cosmological constant would have prevented the formation of galaxies, which are necessary for the existence of observers, and since observers exist this would imply that the cosmological constant cannot have values so large as to prevent the galaxy formation. According to Smolin, in the previous reasoning the point relating to the existence of observers is not necessary and furthermore the principle would be unscientific because it cannot make any predictions and a theory that does not make predictions is unscientific. From Weinberg's point of view, the anthropic principle is not only falsifiable, but has already been tested, for example in the prediction made by Weinberg. In fact, in Weinberg's reasoning the part relating to observers is a fundamental point of the reasoning. If the reasoning had been focused only on the formation of galaxies, then the cosmological constant could assume a value much lower than the maximum allowed, this is because galaxies can be formed even with a small cosmological constant.

Weinberg instead proposed that the value could not be much smaller than the maximum value that made possible the formation of galaxies. For example, if the value found had been zero, the anthropic principle could be discarded since this value was extremely unlikely. A cosmological constant close to the maximum possible value indicates that it has been chosen from among the values compatible with life. Thus Weinberg had falsified the anthropic principle. In addition to Smolin's criticisms of the anthropic principle, there are several others, such as the criticism that it leads to circular reasoning.

According to the anthropic principle, the values of physical constants have the value they have because if they were not such there would be no observers who could verify this. If we ask ourselves why we are here, we come to the conclusion that we are here because the constants are what they are and allow our existence. This obvious circularity of the anthropic principle is broken by the presence of the multiverse. If the multiverse exists, the anthropic principle says that among all possible universes we should be in the subset of those suitable for the appearance of life and observers. By accepting to be observers chosen at random from all possible observers, we come to deduce a multitude of things about our universe, which can be subjected to verification. Other criticisms come from the philosopher Jesus Mosterin. For him the anthropic principle is neither a principle nor an anthropic one. It is a mere tautology that lacks explanatory force, and unable to make predictions. The anthropic principle can lead to inferences but not to explanations and those who use it often confuse these two aspects. Again Mosterin's critique applies to the anthropic principle assuming that the multiverse does not exist. In this case our existence leads us to infer that the laws of physics are compatible with life, but they do not lead us to any explanation.

As already said, in a multiverse things change, and the anthropic principle allows us to explain (not infer) various characteristics of our Universe. This is clear by referring to the application of the principle to the cosmological constant. The principle not only says that observers can exist only for some values of the cosmological constant, but the theory predicts a set of universes with different values of the cosmological constant and only we can find those universes compatible with our existence. Consequently, the cosmological constant in our universe must be expected to have a value compatible with life. We must also expect that in the set of values of the cosmological constant, compatible with life, its value must be one of the most probable. However, for the anthropic principle to have predictive value, there must be a mechanism that produces universes with different constants, a multiverse, and the anthropic principle.

In conclusion, while the anthropic principle alone does not have great predictive power, everything changes when it is combined with a theory that predicts the multiverse. If the need for a multiverse is accepted, the anthropic principle functions as a selection principle: among all the universes envisaged by the theory, it can select those compatible with the presence of observers (intelligent life). Despite this, the anthropic principle cannot be considered as part of science, and at the same time it is not unscientific. It allows us to answer questions that without its use would be metaphysics. We repeat, however, that we must not forget that all this is possible if the idea of the multiverse and the theory that predicts the multiverse is valid and accepted. To date, the two theories that generate multiverses with different constants, the *superstring theory* and *chaotic inflation* are not entirely accepted.

With regard to supersymmetry, in sections 5.5 and 8.4 some of the limitations of this theory are discussed, such as the enormous number of ways to compact dimensions. Not knowing the compactification typical of our universe, the string theory that is proposed as the theory of everything becomes in reality a theory of anything.

Proposed as the fundamental theory to unify gravity and quantum mechanics, it failed in its intent. Today, many scientists believe that the theory is not a solid scientific theory.

As for inflation, although it is accepted by most physicists, a certain part of the community has doubts about it and some of the evidence that would give the certainty of its existence has not been confirmed, as we have seen in section 4.1.

The anthropic principle is not accepted by a large number of physicists who see it unable to give scientific explanations about the Universe apart, as Aczel says (in *Why science does not disprove God*), "*the banal one that things are as they are because they could not be otherwise*". Similar to the case of the multiverse, they hope that a theory of everything will be found that fixes the parameters once and for all and that gives a scientific and not a statistical explanation of why there is life in the Universe. This would lead to the elimination of the anthropic principle. Recalling Penrose's argument on entropy and fine-tuning related to the Big Bang of our Universe, if the anthropic principle can say something in the case of the fine-tuning of constants, it has nothing to say about the fine-tuning related to entropy that we discussed. A particular theory is needed to explain why the Big Bang was as it was. In this case the anthropic principle is completely useless.

Before concluding, I would like to remind that the anthropic principle has also been used as a line of reasoning that leads to the existence of the multiverse. As we have seen, the parameters of our Universe are too well tuned to have emerged by chance. The fact that our existence requires that their values are localized in a narrow range implies that there must be other places where the value of the parameters are not the right ones. If there are other universes, we don't need a creator, because statistics mean that in the myriads of universes, one will have the right parameters that will lead to an evolution with living beings in it. In other words, the anthropic principle (coupled with the multiverse) is used to eliminate the idea that there is a "project" behind our universe.

## Summary: Keynotes

- By examining the constants of the Universe, it can be seen that by varying their values our Universe would be completely different and could not host life. Not all constants are extremely finely regulated such as the value of the initial entropy or the cosmological constant. Some admit variations of a few percentage points before changing the appearance of our Universe.
- Our Universe is expanding at an accelerated rate. The cause of why this occurs is not known. One possibility is that the origin of the acceleration is due to the cosmological constant. If one connects this quantity with the energy of the vacuum, one sees a huge discrepancy between the theoretical predictions and the observations. The range of

values that it can take can be obtained using the anthropic principle. Nevertheless, the anthropic principle does not give a reason for the range of values of the cosmological constant apart from the tautology *"we have that range of values only because we are here to observe it"*.

- There are different forms of the anthropic principle. The weak version of the principle is basically a tautology, the strong one, depending on how it is read, oscillates between a tautology and an unscientific position. The participatory anthropic principle comes to the conclusion that the Universe is created by observer-participants through a complex and "abstruse" principle backward causation. Anthropogenic principles in versions of final cause are considered unacceptable.

- The anthropic principle takes on considerable strength only when it is placed side by side with the concept of multiverse. In this case it acts as a selector between universes. Among all the universes predicted by some theories, it can select those compatible with the presence of observers.

- The validity of the anthropic principle is linked to the existence of a mechanism that generates the multiverse. Examples of this are: string theory and chaotic inflation. The former is today not considered by most physicists as a solid scientific theory, the latter has not been fully verified and one cannot be sure of its existence.

- A case in which the anthropic principle is completely useless is that of the fine-tuning of the Big Bang described by Roger Penrose, linked to the second law of thermodynamics.

- The existence of life leads us to choose between the idea that: 1. either there was a great architect who thought of everything down to the smallest detail, 2. or by chance (even if very unlikely), 3. or because there is a huge number of universes and the anthropic principle tells us that in the one we are living there is the correct combination of parameters. That is, there is a multiverse and the Universe is suitable for life simply by a selection effect.

# CHAPTER 8

# THE MULTIVERSE, THE "GOLDILOCK ENIGMA" AND GOD

*String theory envisions a multiverse in which our universe is one slice of bread in a big cosmic loaf. The other slices would be displaced from ours in some extra dimension of space.*

— Brian Green

It has been known for a long time that the Universe seems to be fit for life. If we consider the existence of only one universe, the coincidences in the constants of physics lead us to think that someone has chosen them so that life appears, that is, that there is a creator. Today this point of view has changed for many physicists and this is due to the emergence of the concept of the *multiverse*. Thanks to the concept of the multiverse, the very strange characteristic of the Universe of being "friendly" to life can be explained simply as a selection effect, without requiring the existence of god. As we have seen when talking about inflation, the theory of the multiverse tells us that the Universe, understood in the classical way, is only a tiny part of a much larger and more complex system: a set of an enormous number of universes, or if you want distinct regions, such as the bubble universes created by chaotic inflation. If these universes differ from each other, life will only be born in those regions or universes with conditions favorable to life. Introducing the multiverse, the answer to the old questions *"why is there something rather than nothing?"*, *"Why do we exist?"*, have a simple answer: *we have won a sort of cosmic lottery and we do not need God to explain our existence.* For this solution to be valid we need a particular multiverse, one in which the physical laws or at least the constants of physics change from one universe to another. There are several paths that lead to the multiverse, not all of which are useful for our purpose of explaining why we exist without resort to a creator.

## 8.1 The "Multiverse" of the Many-worlds Interpretation of Quantum Mechanics

The idea of the multiverse first appeared in quantum mechanics and was proposed by Hugh Everett III in 1957. Everett proposed a new interpretation of quantum mechanics, called the *many-worlds interpretation,* that differed from the Copenhagen interpretation. He tried to eliminate the problem of the collapse of the wave function and to reduce the role of the observer, central to the Copenhagen interpretation of quantum mechanics. In the example of Schrödinger's cat that we made in chapter 6 we saw that when the cat is closed in the box it is in a superposition of two states: live cat and dead cat. When the box is opened, that is, when the measurement is taken, the wave function will collapse and reality will materialize under the eyes of the observer: the cat will be either dead or alive.

In the many-worlds interpretation, the observer and the measured system constitute a single state called "world". At the time of the measurement, the global state is divided into as many worlds as the results of the measurement. In simpler terms, if you carry out an experiment that has two possible results, the Universe will split into two.

In the many-worlds interpretation, the situation is not as paradoxical as in Copenhagen view. In the act of measuring the Universe splits into two: in one the cat is alive and in the other it is dead. Each event is a branch point for the Universe. In chapter 7 we talked about the anthropic principle, the opposite of the *Copernican principle*: our place (role) in the universe is not negligible. In general, the anthropic principle can be used together with the multiverse to explain some characteristics of the Universe we live in, but the quantum multiverse combined with the anthropic principle is not enough to explain the value of the constants of physics or their fine-tuning since they they do not change from Universe to Universe. In other words, if we are in a multiverse made up of universes with different laws or constants, we can expect that for a matter of probability among the many universes ours is the one with the right constants for our survival. In the case of the many worlds theory, the various universes are similar to each other, they have the same constants, and therefore the anthropic argument is substantially unusable. Apart from this aspect, the interpretation of many worlds has had detractors since its origin. The splitting of our world into two every time a decision is made or something happens is hard to digest. The idea that there is a Universe in which Caesar never existed and we lived thousands of years ago and all the other strange possibilties do not intuitively testify in favor of the interpretation to many worlds.

## 8.2 The Multiverse of Chaotic Inflation

In chapter 4 we talked about inflation and in particular about chaotic inflation. In this model, the dynamics of the Universe is dominated by the dynamics of a scalar field, the inflaton. Regions of false vacuum "transit" in the state of true vacuum forming bubbles. These bubbles (regions) are not connected to each other, because space expands at superluminal speed. They constitute disconnected universes that are generated indefinitely. Chaotic inflation therefore generates an infinity of universes and the most interesting thing for us is that the laws of physics vary from universe to universe. This allows to solve the problem of the fine-tuning of constants for simple statistical reasons.

A final point I would like to point out is that in Guth's inflation, as already discussed, there was the problem of how to stop inflation. We have seen that Steinhardt and Linde proposed another model for solving this problem. With eternal and chaotic inflation, we could say that we have gone back: we have a Universe in which inflation never stops. *At this point the question arises whether an eternal inflation with infinite universes is not the result of the inability to stop inflation, rather than a physical reality.*

## 8.3 Flat and Multiverse Universe

Another way of generating a multiverse is based on the fact that our Universe is flat, that is, infinite. Consequently, only a part of the entire Universe can be observed, the so-called observable Universe. We cannot observe further because the expansion occurs at superluminal speed. Moving in an infinite Universe sooner or later we should find a clone of the Earth and its inhabitants. According to Max Tegmark, the closest copy would be at $10^{10^{29}}$ m. Moving a little more, $10^{10^{120}}$ m, you could even find a clone of our Universe. The probability of running into a clone of ourselves although theoretically possible is unlikely since in a Universe based on the Big Bang, the separation between us and our clone is greater than the size of the horizon, which means that not only will we not meet our clone, but we won't be able to communicate with him either. In the case of chaotic inflation, our universe is not infinite, but is located in a very large but finite region. However, remains the problem that the Universe is made up of a huge number of universes. As far as we are concerned, this type of multiverse is similar to the quantum multiverse, since it does not consider a modification of the constants between one Universe and another, and therefore cannot be used for example to estimate the value of constants such as the cosmological one. It can be used to explain coincidences in the material distribution around us. For the anthropic principle to have truly predictive power, a multiverse with constants that change from one universe to another is needed. Such a type of multiverse is provided by the inflation theory and by that of the superstrings.

## 8.4 The Multiverse of String Theory

In chapter 5 we talked about string theory and $M$ theory, also discussing their limits. We have seen that one of the problems is the huge number of ways in which the extra dimensions can be compacted, which makes the theory a theory of anything rather than a TOE (theory of everything). In superstring theory, extra dimensions are rolled up into complex figures called Calabi-Yau spaces (Figure 8.1), six-dimensional spaces, named after the Italian Eugenio Calabi and the Chinese Shing-Tung Yau, and are associated at each space-time point. Figure 8.1 gives an idea of what this space is, approximated and distorted because we are visualizing a six-dimensional space on a two-dimensional sheet of paper.

According to a 2004 Douglas estimate, the number of possible compactification of the extra dimensions is of the order of $10^{500}$ or, according to other authors, even higher. There is a *Calabi-Yau space* for each compactification, and each of these spaces corresponds to a false vacuum (Universe) of the theory. Each false vacuum corresponds to a Universe with physical laws different from the others. The number of possible universes could be between $10^{500}$ and $10^{10^{375}}$, the

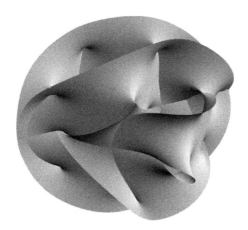

Figure 8.1.   Calabi-Yau spaces. *Source*: Wikipedia

latter value being obtained by Linde. According to Linde, this would provide a scientific justification for the anthropic principle, since it should not postulate the existence of all possible universes, as these are predicted by the theory of chaotic inflation. From other points of view, the huge number of possible compactifications takes away scientific value of the superstring theory. If we don't know how to compact the extra dimensions, no real-world predictions based on that theory can be made. In fact, it has been proposed as a theory of everything, that is, a theory of unification of all forces that explains all the constants of physics in terms of well understood mathematical laws. Such a theory would naturally generate all the parameters of physics that should no longer be obtained from experiments.

Well, a theory that foresees at least $10^{500}$ universes is certainly not a theory of everything, but a theory of anything, and it does not explain our universe.

Superstring theory is a highly mathematized theory. We know that there is a relationship between mathematics and reality, but this relationship is not always valid. Mathematics doesn't always have a real match. *If string mathematics needs many dimensions to work, that doesn't mean that our world is actually made up of many dimensions.* As for the multiverse of string theory, it arises from the inability to find the compactification corresponding to our world. As a consequence, the existence of a huge number of compactifications (Universes) does not necessarily indicate the existence of a large number of universes.

## 8.5 A Multitude of Multiverses

There are other forms of multiverse. Brian Green in his text *The hidden reality. Parallel universes and the deep laws of the Cosmos* mentions nine different types of multiverse, and to recall a few, there would be the *landscape multiverse*, based formed by Calabi-Yau spaces that we have already talked about, the *quantum multiverse* linked to Hugh Everett III's many worlds interpretation of quantum mechanics, the *brane multiverse*, based on the $M$ theory. As already discussed, each *brane* would constitute a Universe. The *simulated multiverse* exists in very powerful computers, which would simulate entire universes. An idea similar to that of the *Matrix*. There would also be the *holographic multiverse*, based on the *holographic principle* which asserts that our three-dimensional universe would be a kind of projection of a two-dimensional reality, like a hologram. By extending the idea to the multiverse, the holographic multiverse is obtained. The dynamics of the inflationary multiverse would be contained within its boundary. The list goes on.

Max Tegmark made a sort of classification of the multiverses. There are four different types of multiverse linked to eternal inflation:

- Type I: Universes similar to each other, but undetectable
- Type II: similar to case I but with different constants of the physical laws and spatial dimensions
- Type III: with the same characteristics as II, and linked to the *multi-world representation of quantum mechanics*.
- Type IV: different forms of the laws of physics. Every mathematical structure has a correspondence in the physical world.

As you can see, the multiverses proposed are certainly not lacking. The problem is that *it is much easier to imagine different types of multiverses, but it is certainly much more complicated to be able to prove that they exist.*

## 8.6 Is the Multiverse Scientific?

Many physicists do not easily accept the possibility of the existence of the multiverse, even if some theories, such as the superstring theory, lead to the multiverse. Indeed, much of the criticism of the multiverse comes from researchers working with superstrings, despite this theory predicts the multiverse. An example is that of Paul Steinhardt, who considers the idea as dangerous, and as already mentioned, despite being one of the fathers of inflation, he promoted a new model of the

Universe because he did not accept the inflationary multiverse. Other researchers like David Gross criticize the multiverse, for other reasons. From his point of view, there is a theory of everything that will explain why constants have the value they have and therefore for him the idea of constants that vary from Universe to Universe is not acceptable together with the multiverse. The theory of everything, if found, is a theory with no free parameters. In this theory all the parameters would be fixed by the theory. In such a theory, God would have no place in the choice of parameters and in how to build the Universe. Physicist John Polkinghorne is one of the criticists of the idea of the multiverse. He writes:

> *Let's recognize these conjectures for what they are. They are not physical, but strictly speaking metaphysical. … By definition these other worlds are unknowable to us. An explanation of equal intellectual respectability … would be that this world is as it is because it is the creation of the will of the Creator who intends to make it so.*

For the philosopher Richard Swinburne it is the "*peak of irrationality*". From another point of view it must be remembered that the multiverse is not only predicted by the many-worlds interpretation of quantum mechanics, inflation or superstring theory, but the combination of the Big Bang and *symmetry breaking* give rise to some form of multiverse. An initially very hot universe that cools down generates domains with different properties. At this point the question arises whether the idea of the multiverse is a scientific idea. As we have seen, in the case of chaotic inflation the universes are so far away that there is no way to think about verifying their existence directly. The space-time between these universes expands at a speed greater than that of light and since we cannot move at such speed we have no way to directly verify the existence of these universes, not taking into account the fact that chaotic inflation would also act on our bodies making them expand and destroy us. Now according to Karl Popper's point of view, anything that is not falsifiable is not scientific, and therefore we should think of the multiverse as an unscientific idea. Wanting to take the side of the supporters of the multiverse, one could think of indirect ways of testing the existence of these universes and if the tests were successful the idea could be considered scientific. Sometimes you can have confidence in an unverifiable idea of a theory that as a whole has been verified and is correct. Let us consider the case of a well known and verified theory, *Quantum Chromodynamics* (QCD). The theory predicts that protons and neutrons are made up of more elementary particles: quarks. The theory also says that it is not possible to observe quarks. From this we should deduce that QCD is not a scientific theory, but in reality it is because it makes many other testable predictions, and many experiments have shown that the predictions are correct. Therefore the QCD is not only scientific but it is also correct.

Similar observations can be made about the General Relativity that can be applied inside black holes, an undetectable region. Similarly, the inflation that the multiverse predicts also makes other predictions that have been verified. This would lead us to think that the theory of the multiverse, if inflation is accepted as scientific, should be considered as scientific. As we have seen, however, this last idea is not accepted by several scientists. Furthermore, criticism and doubts also weigh on inflation.

There are some very eccentric proposals to indirectly prove the existence of the multiverse. One of these is based on the unlikely collision of a universe with ours. In fact, we have already seen that the Universes are located at enormous distances from each other. This would leave some sort of mark on the CMB, but the type of signal would depend on the type of inflation. It could also happen that the push from the collision of the universe next to ours would produce a motion of the galaxies in that area different from that in the rest of the Universe. Some scientists say they have observed this type of "*dark-flow*", but there is considerable skepticism on this point. In the CMB, an anomaly called *cold spot* of about 5–10° is

Figure 8.2.   Cold spot in the CMB.

observed (Figure 8.2). This area could be due to a multiplicity of causes, such as a large void located between us and the cold spot or other more exotic reasons. In a fanciful interpretation, according to Laura Mersin-Houghton, the cold spot could be due to a *quantum entanglement*, such as the one described in Section 6.7, but in this case it would be an entanglement between our universe and another, then separated by inflation.

Another way in which the multiverse theory could be tested is by observing the value of the constants in our universe. Experiments were carried out using quasars to study the fine structure of the spectral lines and determine changes in physical constants. There seems to be no variation of the constants. Another study relates to a uranium deposit in Gabon, which in about two billion years has become a sort of reactor. Also in this case no variations in the constants are observed.

Ultimately, the community of physicists is divided into supporters of the multiverse and opponents. The idea is not directly verifiable and it is not trivial to find indirect evidence of its existence. The indirect tests I mentioned are highly speculative. Although there are supporters of the multiverse, even among them the idea *is clear that it is a "theory" that cannot be verified even in principle.* To conclude, the theory of the multiverse could clash with *Occam's Razor*, which says that *"all things being equal, the simplest explanation is to be preferred.*" In other words, among the various explanations of an event, one must always choose the simplest one, not in the sense of the most banal that comes to mind, but the one that appears reasonably true without looking for unnecessary complications by adding additional and unnecessary elements. *Why would the idea of a multiverse clash with Occam's razor? Because to explain the existence of a universe in which life exists, a simpler idea is eliminated, such as the existence of a project favorable to the appearance of life, or another simple hypothesis not yet formulated or the idea that everything happened by chance, giving rise to an infinite number of parameters and hypotheses necessary for the birth of the multiverse.* Richard Dawkins is known to have used Occam's razor in his book *The God Delusion*, arriving at conclusions opposite to the previous ones. According to him "*one cannot become much more complex than an almighty God*". At first glance, one might think that Dawkins is right: what is more complex than an infinite mind? But the same criticism can be leveled at the multiverse, requiring an infinite amount of unverifiable information. Is it simpler an infinite invisible God or an infinite set of invisible universes?

## 8.7 The Multiverse and God

In chapter 7 we saw that our Universe appears to be calibrated for life. If our Universe were the only one, logic would lead us to think that it was designed by a higher being. The idea that the Universe arose by chance, knowing that several parameters are subject to fine-tuning and their values seem to have been specially chosen, is not easy to accept. The case of the cosmological constant that generates a force opposite to gravity with a "sensitivity" of $1/10^{120}$ is enough to make us discard the idea of a random origin of the Universe. As Freeman Dyson said

> *The more I examine the universe and the details of its architecture, the more evidence I find that the universe in some sense must have known we were coming*

In the laws of physics there are numerical coincidences that seem to have worked to make the Universe habitable.

Andrei Linde referring to fine-tuning said that

*We have a lot of really, really strange coincidences, and all of these coincidences are such that they make life possible,*

adding that the multiverse gives the possibility to answer questions about the fine-tuning that allows life on Earth. The multiverse theory saves those who are not willing to believe in a creator from embarrassment. The multiverse, together with other hypotheses, such as the origin of the Universe from nothing, and the like, has been called *"the last God of the atheist"* and used by non-believers to avoid arguments (such as the problem of the origin of 'Universe, or fine-tuning) that could be used in favor of the existence of God. Although there are several branches of physics (quantum mechanics, and cosmology) that justify the existence of the multiverse, this argument remains one of the most interesting and controversial of current science. The idea of the multiverse and its consequences have not remained confined to science, but have philosophical and theological implications. As seen, there is currently no scientific evidence proving the existence of the multiverse.

Nonetheless, many scientists, and philosophers have hailed the multiverse as the element that exempts us from having to believe in God. For non-believers, the multiverse is like a sort of last resort, a position of safety from which to criticize believers accused by atheists to have faith in something without tangible evidence. To tell the truth, the same criticism could be leveled by believers against atheists, given that the multiverse does not seem to have tangible proof and it does not seem that the future will bring any. Even if the multiverse existed, there remains one question to answer: how did it originate? As Stephen Hawking wrote in his *"A brief history of time"*,

*Many people do not like the idea that time has a beginning, probably because it smacks of divine intervention.*

Similarly, in the opinion of Steven Weinberg, *"the oscillating model ... nicely avoids the problem of Genesis"*. In other words, an eternal universe would be attractive because not having to explain the origin, it eliminates the problem of divine intervention.

In fact, as we will see in section 9.1, even seemingly eternal universes, such as the multiverse generated by chaotic inflation, the cyclical universe of Steinhardt and Turok and others, actually had a beginning. So even if our Universe were an infinitesimal part of a multiverse, the latter would have to be born, and there would remain the problem of explaining how this happened. In other words, the shadow of the creator also extends over the multiverse.

Another important point to remember is that when infinity is given access to any topic, everything becomes possible. As already said if we are in an infinite universe, moving in it sooner or later we should find a clone of the Earth and also a clone of ourselves. This idea, however *"strange and implausible"*, for Tegmark, is an obligatory consequence of an infinite universe. To show the power of infinity, there is even the so-called *infinite monkey theorem* which states that a monkey who presses the keys of a keyboard at random and for an infinite time, will be able to compose any text. Richard Dawkins, using a program that randomly generates letters of the alphabet, has verified that the probability for a monkey to write a sentence of 28 characters is equal to 1 divided by 10,000 million million million million million million million. It is evident that the idea of the monkey typing, beating to infinity is a forced and impossible argument, but it only serves to show how powerful the concept of infinity is. Infinity is such a powerful concept that everything that can happen is possible. To use this concept in cosmology one should be sure that the processes, the theories, which can produce an infinite universe, or the multiverse, have solid foundations. As already seen, the theories that predict a multiverse in which it is possible to give an explanation for fine-tuning are theories that predict universes with different constants from one to the other, namely the theory of superstrings and chaotic inflation.

We have seen that string theory has problems finding what the compactification is relative to our universe and that there are at least $10^{500}$ different possible compactifications, or false vacuums, corresponding to the same number of universes. *In other words, the multiverse of superstring theory arises from the inability to find a single theory relating to a single compactification. The fact that we cannot, by our limits, find a single compactification does not mean that there should be $10^{500}$ compatifications and as many universes.*

Beyond this we have already discussed that there is little or no evidence of the scientific soundness of string theory. Regarding inflation we saw in section 5.1 that although many scientists accept the theory, there is no direct evidence of its real existence. The *"smoking gun"* of the existence of inflation, the primordial gravitational waves, have not been found. Nothing is known about the field that originated inflation and so on. Replacing the multiverse to God is equivalent to replacing a hypothetical being with a hypothetical model and this does not solve our problems. In fact, as one can ask who created God, one can also ask who created the multiverse. We need a mechanism that generates universes. We have seen that one possibility is chaotic inflation which, with the laws of quantum mechanics, generates bubble universes. This does not solve the problem because one may wonder where the laws of quantum mechanics come from, and those of gravity and the causal structure of space-time on which the laws depend, which allow inflation. If the multiverse were supposed to be generated by theory $M$, it and its mathematical structure must be accepted as given without explanation. The situation is similar to the anecdote of the infinite tower of turtles told by Stephen Hawking in his bestseller *A short story of time* (and taken up by Paul Davies in *The Goldilocks enigma*)

*A well-known scientist (some say it was Bertrand Russell) once gave a public lecture on astronomy. He described how the earth orbits around the sun and how the sun, in turn, orbits around the center of a vast collection of stars called our galaxy. At the end of the lecture, a little old lady at the back of the room got up and said: "What you have told us is rubbish. The world is really a flat plate supported on the back of a giant tortoise." The scientist gave a superior smile before replying, "What is the tortoise standing on?" "You're very clever, young man, very clever," said the old lady. "But it's turtles all the way down!"*

This problem often arises when trying to give a complete explanation of reality. For example, if we assume that God is the creator of the world, we can ask ourselves who created God and so on to infinity. If you want to avoid a problem of *"regression to infinity"* it is necessary to assume that at some point there is something given that does not need explanations. It is necessary, in the words of Paul Davies, to accept a *"levitating super-turtle"* on which everything rests. An example are the axioms of geometry that represent the super-turtle and solve the problem of infinite regression. So proponents of theories like the theory of everything will have to accept the equations of the theory as their super turtle. The same thing must happen for supporters of the multiverse theory who will have to accept, as mentioned, a theory that creates universes, quantum mechanics, relativity etc., as their super-turtle.

Ultimately, the multiverse could be a solution to the problem of the fine-tuning of constants and replace the idea of a designed universe. The basic problem is that the multiverse is a highly speculative concept whose existence cannot be verified even in principle. It is a matter of choosing between an infinite invisible God or an infinite set of invisible universes.

## Summary: Keynotes

- Several physical theories predict the existence of the multiverse: an interpretation of quantum mechanics, inflation, and string theory. It should be noted that predictions are usually related to a problem of theory in consideration. In the case of quantum mechanics the problem is related to the theory of measurement. In the case of inflation, the problem is the impossibility of stopping it. In the case of string theory the problem is related to the fact that we do not know the right compactification for our Universe.

- The existence of the multiverse cannot be practically tested, because the expansion of each universe is superluminal. Some ideas of verification have been proposed, though not very convincing. From the Popperian point of view, the multiverse should therefore be cataloged as unscientific.

- If only one universe existed, the fine-tuning of the physical constants would lead us to the conclusion that there is a project for the origin, the evolution of the universe and the birth of life. In a multiverse, the fine-tuning of constants can be explained in a statistical way: in an infinity of universes in one or some the constants must be those necessary for life to appear. Of course, the question always remains: who created the multiverse? To this must be added the impossibility of being able to verify its existence.

CHAPTER 9

# A UNIVERSE FROM NOTHING?

*The world embarrasses me,*

*and I cannot dream that this watch*

*exists and has no watchmaker.*

— Voltaire

The problem of the formation of the Universe and what existed before its origin has affected all cultures of all times, as evidenced by the multitude of cosmologies that have been invented over the centuries. The answer to the question of the origin of the cosmos have been linked for millennia to mysticism and religions. There are myriads of eschatologies, doctrines aimed at investigating the destiny of the individual, of mankind and of the universe. With the evolution of societies, more philosophical and rational arguments were sought. Today, as is well known, the most popular scientific theory is that of the Big Bang. However, this theory has problems describing what happened in the initial stages of the universe's formation, from the initial time to Planck's time, corresponding to $10^{-43}$ s after the Big Bang. The model does not even explain what there was before the Big Bang and an answer that is often given to this question is that it makes no sense to ask what there was before the Big Bang since space and time originated with the Big Bang. That is, the modern point of view is not much ahead of the point of view of Saint Augustine that we described in section 1.2, namely that *the world was not created in time but with time*. In a cyclic universe this point of view is incorrect because before the Big Bang there was simply another universe like ours.

145

## 9.1 Did the Universe have a Beginning?

Leaving aside the question of what existed before the Big Bang, the question of how the Universe originated remains the most fundamental of cosmology. The question assumes that the Universe had an origin, but it can be assumed that the Universe has always existed and always will be. In this case there would have been no origin, only evolution.

At the same time we have evidence that the Universe almost certainly began almost 14 billion years ago. Was that the "absolute beginning" or was there something before it? This is one of the questions that Alexander Vilenkin asks himself and the answer is not trivial. According to Vilenkin, the Universe had a distinct beginning, although he is unable to determine when it began. For example, in a chaotic inflationary Universe the 14 billion years we measure may be those relating to the Big Bang in our Universe, but every other Universe will have a Big Bang at a different time.

There are a number of cosmologies that, unlike the Big Bang theory, argue that the Universe did not have an origin. One of these is the theory of the cyclic universe which had neither a beginning nor an end. In this type of Universe there is an expansion phase followed by a collapse in a Big Crunch,[1] which originates, as in a new Big Bang, a new Universe.

In a universe of this type, the Big Bang that we "observe" could be the one relating to the last Big Crunch.

After the solution of the equations of General Relativity, in 1922 Friedman had found three solutions, one of which described the universe as cyclic, that is, made up of a succession of Big Bangs and Big Crunchs, similar to the situation of a ball moving away from the ground up to a maximum height followed by a fall to the ground and a bounce (Big Bounce). This was also one of the models designed by Richard Tolman. Each bounce would have generated a singularity that could not be described by General Relativity. One of the problems

---

[1] The Big Crunch model argues that the Universe will reach a maximum of expansion and then collapse on itself.

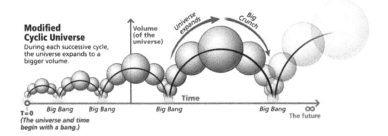

Figure 9.1.    Cyclic universe with an increase in volume at each cycle due to the accumulation of entropy. The contraction phase is the Big Crunch.

of the model is to explain what happens to entropy, that is, the degree of disorder, in the various phases. The initial entropy of the Universe, at the first Big Bang, was low and grew as its size increased. In the recollapse phase, entropy does not reverse its course, as galaxies do, but as noted by Tolman in 1931, it continues to grow. Consequently, at each cycle there will be an increase in entropy with a consequent increase in the maximum size and in the time between successive cycles (see Figure 9.1).

By adding a cosmological constant, which describes the accelerated expansion, cyclicality is eliminated from the equations of General Relativity. So with the discovery of the accelerated expansion of the universe, Tolman's universe was discarded. However, there are conflicting theses.[2] So, if we want a cyclic Universe it is necessary to find a way to decrease entropy. In 1999 Paul Steinhardt and Neil Turok believed they could find a possible solution based on string theory[3] in the *ecpirotic model*, already described in section 5.1. In this model there is a sequence of identical cycles of expansion and contraction. In Steinhardt's description

---

[2] Frampton in 2015 showed that entropy can be canceled from one cycle to another, and other physicists have found various solutions to solve the entropy problem.

[3] More precisely, the M theory, which conveys the five string theories into a single theory.

*In this picture, space and time exist forever. The big bang is not the beginning of time. Rather, it is a bridge to a pre-existing contracting era. The Universe undergoes an endless sequence of cycles in which it contracts in a big crunch and re-emerges in an expanding big bang, with trillions of years of evolution in between. The temperature and density of the universe do not become infinite at any point in the cycle; indeed, they never exceed a finite bound (about a trillion trillion degrees). No inflation has taken place since the big bang. The current homogeneity and flatness were created by events that occurred before the most recent big bang. The seeds for galaxy formation were created by instabilities arising as the Universe was collapsing towards a big crunch, prior to our big bang.*

The studies on this model have continued until arriving at two different possible models, one based on quantum mechanics, proposed by Turok and Gielen, and a classical model proposed by Steinhardt. In both, the singularity is avoided by obtaining the Big Bounce.

Another type of cyclic universe has been proposed by Roger Penrose, the so-called *conformal cyclic cosmology*. According to Roger Penrose, in a universe that has reached thermal death, the microscopic could have influences on the macroscopic, causing the dead universe to give rise to a new Big Bang. The entropy problem is solved by assuming that the information and therefore also the entropy is lost in the final evaporation of the huge black holes that dominate the universe after $10^{100}$ years. Furthermore, the model predicts that the collision between black holes should produce gravitational waves visible as concentric rings on the CMB. According to Penrose and Gurzadyan, these rings are visible in the CMB map of the WMAP satellite. There are other cosmologies that do not admit a singularity. One of them is the superstring theory. According to the cosmology of superstring theory, also called *pre-big bang cosmology*, the Big Bang was not the origin of everything but only an instant in which a state of very high density performs a sort of rebound into a state of rapidly decreasing density. In superstring theory there is a fundamental length that can be considered as the size of a point in space. This dimension is equal to $10^{-35}$ m which ultimately represents the smallest radius of the space. Superstring cosmology describes a flat and almost empty Universe at the very beginning of the Universe, with similar characteristics in the future. Our Universe emerged from an eternally existing pre-Universe when density reached its maximum value in a big crunch, which from our point of view is a Big Bang (see Figure 9.1). All this was followed by the inflationary phase and the accelerating Universe that we observe today. So there is no beginning in superstring theory. There is a concurrent theory the *quantum loop theory* (LQG), which we have already talked about. When it is applied to the Universe it gives results in some ways similar. As already seen, according to this theory, space-time consists of rings of $10^{-35}$ m size, which can contain a finite amount of energy. Therefore, as in the superstring theory, there is a minimum dimension under which one cannot go down. In loop quantum theory, space is discrete. This theory, similarly to the superstring theory, does not admit the singularity of the Big Bang. The predicted universe is a variant of the oscillating universe. The universe expands to a maximum and then collapses again. We pass from a pre-universe of eternal duration, a rebound at initial time (t = 0) and an infinite universe. The Universe described by the theory has no beginning or end. The universes described by LQG and string theory are similar but there are differences that could be verified experimentally. Another theory in which the Universe would seem to have no origin is chaotic inflation.

As we have seen, in this theory, regions subject to inflation are produced more rapidly than regions not subject to inflation. Inflation would be infinite in the future and in the past. In Linde's words

> It seems likely that the universe is an eternal, self-reproducing entity divided into many mini-universes, with low-energy physics and perhaps even dimensionality differing from one to the other.

There are other proposals for cyclic universes such as the Baum-Frampton model. This model is linked to that of the Big Rip, according to which the dark energy of the universe exceeding a certain value would produce such a violent acceleration as to destroy all matter in the universe. In the Baum-Frampton model an instant before the Big Rip ($10^{-27}$ s) space would divide into a large number of subspaces, independent volumes, correlated to observable universes. Such mini universes containing neither matter, energy and entropy would contract and each would give rise to a new Big Bang and a new universe. A multitude of universes would then be created, that is, a multiverse, as in the scenario of chaotic inflation and in string theory. Apparently these cyclical universes shouldn't have a beginning, but according to Alexander Vilenkin and Audrey Mithani this is not the case. In 2012 Alexander Vilenkin and Audrey Mithani dealt with the problem of the origin of the Universe, using three scenarios that apparently should not have singularity and exist forever: *the cyclical model of Steinhardt and Turok, eternal inflation* and the so-called *"emergent universe"* that exists for a very long period of time as a *"static seed"* before expanding. Vilenkin and Mithani have shown that all three types of universe, although apparently without origin, have a beginning.

In the Steinhardt and Turok model, entropy increases with each cycle, leading to *"thermal death"* unless the volume of the universe increases with each cycle. In this case we are dealing with an expanding universe to which the so-called *Borde-Guth-Vilenkin theorem* applies which says that any universe that has expanded in its history cannot be infinite in the past, that is, it must have a beginning. Similarly, inflation, according to the Borde-Guth-Vilenkin theorem, cannot be eternal in the past, although it is in the future. As for the third model, the "emerging universe", introduced, among others, by George Ellis, it can exist in a stable configuration for a very long time, and then suddenly expand, similar to an egg in a phase of extremely long incubation. According to Vilenkin and Mithani during the long waiting phase this universe could collapse to one point and vanish. Thus, it does not have an infinite duration. From these examples the two authors concluded that even seemingly eternal universes must have a beginning. The idea of a beginning has often been opposed. As we have already seen, and as Hawking clearly wrote, *many people do not like the idea that time has a beginning probably because it smacks of divine intervention.* For Eddington, the idea of a beginning was repulsive. Weinberg himself, and several other scientists, prefer a beginningless universe. The problem is obviously the fact that if any Universe is to have a beginning, we can ask ourselves how it originated and this can make the idea of a creator pop up again.

## 9.2 The Geometry of our Universe

The attempt to determine the geometry of our Universe goes all the way back to Gauss. In the first half of the nineteenth century he tried to prove that the Universe is not Euclidean by measuring the angles of a triangle formed by the peaks of three mountains (Brocken, Hoher Hagen, and Inselsberg) in the Gottingen region of Germany. Obviously he obtained that the sum of the angles was 180 degrees as in a Euclidean universe, given the small scale used. This idea was applied only a few decades ago, through some space missions, using scales much larger than those used by Gauss. The method is based on the determination of the size of the anisotropies in the CMB (see Figure 2.1). These anisotropies have been studied, as already mentioned by the BOOMERANG balloon, by the WMAP satellites and by PLANCK and their physical dimensions have been found. The conversion into apparent angular dimensions depends on the geometry since in the theory of General Relativity space-time is curved by the presence of matter and energy. Depending on the material content, the universe, as described in Chapter 1, can have three different geometries: closed universe (positive curvature), if $\Omega > 1$, flat universe (null curvature), if $\Omega = 1$, hyperbolic universe (curvature negative), if $\Omega < 1$.

In a flat Universe the dimensions of these regions are about $1^0$. As shown in Figure 9.2 (left side), in a universe with

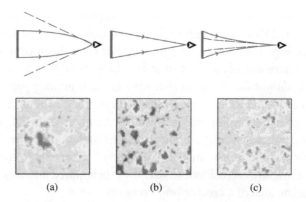

Figure 9.2.   Inhomogeneity in the CMB and geometry of the space. In the three upper figures the thick lines in brown represent the dimensions of an inhomogeneity on the CMB, the thin lines in brown the way in which light propagates in a closed, flat and open Universe, and the black dashed lines the angle subtended by geometry into consideration. In a flat Universe, inhomogeneity subtends an angle of 1 degree. In a closed Universe the subtended angle is greater (panel a) (>1°), while in an open Universe (panel c), the angle is smaller (<1°) than in a flat Universe (1°) (panel b). Cold and warm zones appear larger in a closed Universe, and smaller in an open Universe, than in a flat Universe. This is seen in the lower part of the figure. Source: Lawrence Berkley Cosmology Group / Laboratories.

positive curvature, the angle under which the inhomogeneity is seen is greater than $1^0$ and in a universe with negative curvature would be less than $1^0$ (right side of Figure 9.2). The measurements with the quoted satellites indicate that our Universe is represented by case b, and that therefore it has zero curvature and is flat, that is $\Omega_{total} = 1$ (Figure 9.2, central part).

Another way to determine the geometry of the universe is to simulate the characteristics of the CMB map in different universes and compare them with the observations of the same, as shown in Figure 9.3 which compares the CMB map of the BOOMERANG experiment, with simulations (the three boxes under the BOOMERANG map). The square that most closely resembles the BOOMERANG map is the central one that corresponds to a flat Universe. So from the comparison it is clear that our universe has a flat geometry.

A more precise way to establish, with an accuracy of about 1%, the type of Universe we live in starting from maps like the

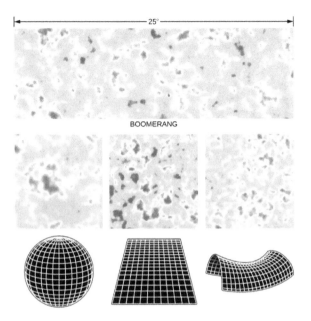

Figure 9.3. Comparison between BOOMERANG data, top panel, with simulations, central panel, of a closed (left), flat (center) and open (right) universe. Source: adapted from a NASA figure.

one in Figure 2.1 is to obtain the so-called *power spectrum of the temperature anisotropies* shown in Figure 9.4.

In Figure 9.4 the red points represent the data obtained from the PLANCK satellite, while the green line represents the forecast related to a flat Universe. According to the 2015 PLANCK satellite data (Figure 9.4) it is found that $\Omega = \rho/\rho_c = 1.0023 \pm 0.0054$. This result confirms that the Universe, within a small error, is flat and therefore the curvature is zero.

## 9.3 A Zero Energy Universe

A spontaneous question at this point is: how can the Universe be flat if the stars, galaxies, and mass in general distort it locally? The only answer to this question is that there is something that produces an opposite distortion, so that the entire Universe has a zero curvature. Recalling Einstein's

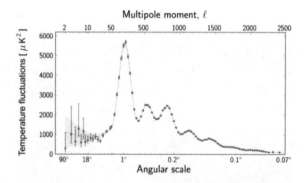

Figure 9.4.   Power spectrum of temperature anisotropies, or sound spectrum of the universe. Source: PLANCK collaboration.

relationship between mass and energy ($E = mc^2$), the energy within the universe behaves like mass and must be taken into account. So if you want to understand why the Universe is flat, you have to take into account all the mass-energy that is in it. It can be understood that there must be two forms of mass-energy: one positive and one negative that balance each other, as we will see.

Returning to the result that the Universe is flat, $\Omega = 1$, it is possible to connect this result with the energy of the entire Universe, using the so-called *Newtonian cosmology*. In 1934 Milne and McCrea showed that in the case of a universe without pressure the equations of relativistic cosmology could be re-obtained with classical mechanics. Their approach can also be modified to take pressure into account, as in the relativistic case. Obviously from the conceptual point of view there are inconsistencies because a Newtonian cosmology assumes the action at a distance (instantaneous) between bodies, however from a practical point of view it is a more intuitive approach than the relativistic one. In this approach it is easy to show that the total energy of the Universe is related to the curvature and the density parameter $\Omega$. It is found that if the energy E is greater than zero ($E > 0$) it results $\Omega < 1$, if the energy is less than zero, $E < 0$ it results $\Omega > 1$ and finally if the energy is zero, $E = 0$, it turns out $\Omega = 1$, that is a flat Universe has zero gravitational energy.

This result gives us a more intuitive view of the three behaviors of Friedman's solutions described in chapter 1. Suppose we are on Earth and throw a ball upwards. The energy of the ball consists of *kinetic* (movement) and *gravitational energy*, due to the attraction of the earth. If we throw the ball upwards with a speed of less than 11.2 km/s, called *escape velocity*, the minimum speed for an object to leave the Earth by overcoming its gravitational attraction, the ball will fall back. In this case the total energy of the ball will be less than zero, $E < 0$. The same thing happens in Friedman's closed universe (having $\Omega > 1$): there is an expansion followed by a collapse (see Figure 1.1). If the ball has a velocity greater than the escape velocity, it will never return to Earth. In this case the energy will be greater than zero, $E > 0$. This corresponds to the case of a hyperbolic universe ($\Omega < 1$) in general relativity, which will expand forever (see figure 1.1). If the velocity is equal to the escape velocity, that is, the kinetic energy is equal to the potential one, we will have $E = 0$. The ball will leave the Earth without returning to it. We find ourselves in the case of the flat universe ($\Omega = 1$). So a flat Universe will have total energy equal to zero. This is because (continuing the analogy with the ball) the kinetic energy is positive, while the gravitational energy is negative, and they have the same and opposite value.[4] Returning to the initial discourse, this explains why the Universe, despite local distortions, as a whole has a flat geometry. The previous discussion also highlighted how the curvature that appears in general relativity is related to the total Newtonian energy and how in a flat Universe the total gravitational energy is zero. This is because, repeating what has been said, the kinetic energy linked to the movement, which is positive, is canceled out with the negative one of gravitational attraction. The fact that the total gravitational energy of the Universe is zero is of fundamental importance for its generation.

---

[4] It is interesting to highlight that the physics that describes the Universe, within the limits of small speeds compared to those of light and masses not too large, is the same physics that we have described for the balls.

## 9.4 The Universe: A Free Meal

As we saw in the previous section, the total gravitational energy of our Universe or its mass-energy are equal to zero. If we look at the starry night this concept seems strange because the Universe appears to be full of mass. Discussing inflation we have seen that the Universe was generated by the exponential expansion of a very small region of space. This idea seems counterintuitive. How can a microscopic region undergo such a transformation that it becomes a region as large as our Universe or even larger, with enough matter, energy, space, to allow us to explain what we observe? Similarly, in the case of the cosmological constant that produces an accelerated expansion of the Universe, how can the energy density remain constant? This implies that as the size of the Universe increases, energy grows. The principle of energy conservation seems to be no longer respected. As we have already seen in section 4.1, initially the Universe contained a scalar field, similar to the Higgs or the quintessential field, called inflaton. The latter is the quantum version of the cosmological constant. The Universe was in a state of false vacuum of the field. This scalar field, like the cosmological constant, or the vacuum energy, produces an accelerated expansion, as it produces antigravity. Why does this field produce antigravity? In Newton's theory, gravity is generated by mass. In general relativity, mass is a source of gravity, but pressure is also a source of gravity. If the pressure is great enough it can even rival the gravity generation of mass-energy. A scalar field has a pressure comparable to its energy and it can produce antigravity because it has negative pressure.

A negative pressure, although it may seem a strange thing is quite familiar to physicists: it is *tension*. For example, a piece of plastic stretched in all directions has negative pressure. Ultimately a scalar field generates antigravity due to its negative pressure and gravity due to its energy. However, the antigravity produced is three times greater than the gravity produced and therefore a scalar field produces a net effect of antigravity. The question posed previously, where does all the energy to allow the energy density to remain constant during the exponential expansion of the Universe come from is linked to the negative pressure. If we consider a balloon, the gas inside it exerts pressure on the surface of the gas. In this way, work is done on the balloon. Such work causes the gas to lose energy and cool. The empty space, unlike the case of the balloon, is endowed with negative pressure. This produces two effects: on the one hand the negative pressure gives rise to antigravity that makes the Universe expand, on the other hand when something with negative pressure expands, it does not lose energy, on the contrary it gains it. This is because due to the negative pressure the Universe exerts work on empty space during its expansion. As a consequence of this work, the energy density of space remains constant even if the Universe expands. So any infinitely small region of space to which quantum properties provide energy, can expand exponentially to include a Universe like ours and be flat. In the process, the total energy of the field in an expanding region of the universe will grow with the expansion, while the total energy of the Universe will remain zero. Due to the negative pressure when the Universe expands, the expansion transfers energy into space. At the end of inflation, the energy contained in space is transformed into particles and radiation. More precisely, at the end of inflation the inflation field decays, begins to oscillate around the minimum of the potential (see figure 4.3) producing a heating phase, dubbed *reheating*, the emission of an enormous quantity of heat in Universe. Thanks to the well-known Einstein formula $E = mc^2$, all the heat emitted can be transformed into particles. So inflation starting from a very small region will give us a Universe full of radiation, matter and total gravitational energy very close to zero. The Universe is the *"ultimate free meal"*, in Guth's words. A Universe generated from nothing. As already mentioned, inflation also generated the seeds from which cosmic structures were formed. Quantum fluctuations at the beginning of inflation are amplified to such an extent that at the end of inflation they become the density perturbations observed in the CMB (Figure 2.1). In a certain sense, in addition to saying that we are stardust, we could also say that we are children of quantum fluctuations. Ultimately, our observable Universe began from a microscopic region of empty space, in the quantum sense, and expanded to the enormous scales we know of, filled with radiation and matter without energy being expended. One might wonder at this point if inflation really generates universes out of *nothing*. To answer this question, we must ask ourselves what is meant by *nothing*. The tiny region of space from which the Universe originated is subject to the laws of physics. Quantum mechanics tells us that that tiny region of space is not really "nothingness". It is full of quantum fluctuations to which an energy is associated. In addition to quantum fluctuations, that tiny region is made up of space and space is governed by the laws of physics. So inflation does not create a universe out of nothing. We need to take another step and show how space originated and where the laws of physics arose.

## 9.5 Quantum Cosmology

A very interesting aspect of quantizing the gravitational degrees of freedom is that related to quantum cosmology, which attempts to study the effects of quantum mechanics on models that study the formation and evolution of the Universe after the Big Bang. One direction of study is that of determining an equation similar to that of Schrödinger for the *wave function of the Universe*, a wave function that governs both material fields and space-time geometry. This equation is known as the Wheeler-de Witt equation, proposed in 1967 by John Archibald Wheeler and Bryce de Witt.

Just as the solution of the Schrödinger equation is the wave function, so the solution of the Wheeler-de Witt equation is the so-called *wave function of the universe*.[5]

---

[5] While in the case of the Schrödinger equation the wave function is a probability density, in the generic case of quantum cosmology the meaning of the wave function of the universe is not so trivial. This is because the Universe constitutes everything that exists and a distinction cannot be made between

The difficulty of finding solutions to this equation soon became evident. In 1982, physicist Amitabha Sen undertook an attempt to modify general relativity so that it was similar to the theories of other fundamental forces. The work begun by Sen was completed by Abhay Ashtekar. Between 1987 and 1988 Ted Jacobson, Lee Smolin and Carlo Rovelli used the ideas of Ashtekar, and Sen to find exact solutions of the Wheeler-de Witt equation, creating *loop quantum gravity*, which as we have seen is a theory that attempts to quantize gravity. In the case of a particle whose evolution of the wave function is to be known, many solutions are obtained using the Schrödinger equation. It is necessary to have information on the *initial quantum state*, also called *boundary conditions*. The same thing happens with the Wheeler-de Witt equation. There are several proposals for the initial quantum state of the Universe (such as those of Hartle-Hawking or Vilenkin), and each leads to different solutions.

A question that could be asked is why it is necessary to apply quantum mechanics, which usually applies to microscopic systems, to the Universe. In the Big Bang cosmology the Universe is expanding and therefore it was smaller in the past. As we saw in section 2.1, just after Planck's time the cosmological horizon was of the order of $10^{-35}$ m which is much smaller than the size of a proton, equal to $10^{-15}$ m. So at that time classical mechanics could not be applied because quantum effects dominated. Does *quantum cosmology* give its own answer to the question *"where did it all come from"*? As we will see in the next section, describing the Universe in joint terms of general relativity and quantum mechanics, that is, in terms of quantum cosmology, leads to the idea that the Universe originated from nothing through *quantum tunneling*.

---

the system being studied and the observer, as in quantum mechanics. A probabilistic interpretation can only be recovered in simplified treatment of quantum cosmology. Another thing to remember is that the wave function of the universe and the equations of quantum gravity do not depend on time.

## 9.6 A Universe from Nothing?

Inflation explains how the Universe could have arisen from a small region of space teeming with quantum fluctuations without consuming energy. The remaining problems are: a) how space and the laws governing the Universe arose?; b) how inflation originated? Quantum cosmology attempts to explain how space and the Universe originated. The answer of quantum cosmology is that the Universe originated through quantum tunneling, out of nothing. The idea of the origin of the Universe from nothing, or rather from quantum fluctuations, was first published by Edward Tryon in 1973 in Nature.[6] In his article Tryon considered a closed universe in which all conserved quantities had a null value. For example, energy is the most important quantity that is conserved in nature: it can neither be created nor destroyed, but only transformed from one form to another. In his article Tryon assumed that the energy in the universe was zero. Since energy is a conserved quantity it cannot be created, and if it is zero as Tryon thought it was not necessary for it to be created. The fact that the energy was zero could be due to the fact that the energy linked to mass and movement, which is positive, was equaled by the negative energy of the gravitational field. Tryon also referred to an argument by P. Bergmann that a closed universe should have zero energy. Energy is not the only quantity that is conserved. There are two types of conserved quantities, *discrete and continuous* quantities. Discrete quantities are those that characterize elementary particles, such as electric charge, baryon and lepton number, etc. According to him, conservation laws should have implied that a universe appearing out of nothing is made up of an equal part of matter and antimatter. Today we know that our universe is basically made up of matter and, as seen in section 3.4, the reasons for the matter antimatter asymmetry are not entirely clear.

---

[6] Pascual Jordan had suggested the idea several years earlier, arguing that the vacuum energy is zero due to the cancellation of the negative energy of the gravitational field and the positive energy of mass and as a consequence, in his opinion, a star could originate from quantum without violating the conservation of energy.

Leaving aside this problem, if all conserved quantities had zero value, the Universe could have appeared out of nothing. Tryon referred to the fluctuations of the vacuum, that is, the appearance and disappearance, for a short time, of electrons, positrons and photons from the vacuum. So if all conserved quantities were zero, the universe could have been a fluctuation of the vacuum. As is known and as can be understood from the discussion, there are some problems in Tryon's argument, but the basic idea of the birth of the universe from the quantum vacuum has been followed and improved by a multitude of physicists.

We have seen that quantum cosmology poses the problem of the origin of the Universe. This problem can be studied in terms of solutions to the Wheeler-de Witt equation. As we have seen, to solve the equation we need the initial state of the Universe and we have seen that there are two proposals, that of Hartle-Hawking and that of Vilenkin. The *Hartle-Hawking state* describes a universe born from nothing with no initial singularity, an initial state without borders. Such a universe would be self-sufficient and self-created. The authors used the concept of imaginary time (introduced by Feynman), to eliminate the singularity, and used the technique of *sum on histories* (already mentioned) or *path integral* to calculate the wave function of the universe, which satisfies the equation of Wheeler-de Witt. Vilenkin used a different initial state for the universe to solve the Wheeler-de Witt equation.

In discursive terms, we can summarize the origin of the Universe described by Vilenkin in the following way. Suppose we have a spherical Universe filled with vacuum energy (which creates repulsion) and matter (which creates attraction). Let's consider the Universe at rest (without expansion or contraction). Evolution depends on the size of the Universe at that instant. If the radius is very small, for general relativity, the attraction will prevail and the Universe will collapse to a point. On the other hand, if the radius is large, repulsive gravity will prevail and the Universe will enter a phase of inflation. Now, in classical physics, the Universe cannot go from a state of collapse to one of inflation. To do this, energy would be needed. Alexander Vilenkin in a 1982 and 1985 paper used

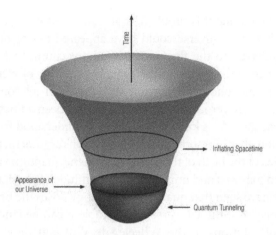

Figure 9.5. Quantum tunneling scheme from nothing that could have given rise to our space-time. Source: Pam Jeffries.

quantum mechanics to solve the problem. In quantum mechanics, everything that can happen happens with a certain probability. The transition between the two states can take place through tunneling. In other words, our tiny universe, destined to collapse, tunneled into the energy barrier of the two states, going from the collapsing state to inflationary one.

The most interesting thing is that the probability of tunneling is not zero even if the radius of the Universe is zero. So a point, of zero size, could tunnel to a radius which would then have allowed it to enlarge and enter an inflationary phase. In other words, it would seem that a Universe is created from nothing. The nothing we are talking about here is not that of inflation. As Vilenkin writes in the 1985 article

by

*"nothing" I mean the absence of classical space-time,*

and then specifies

*..one can create an intuitive picture of the view that opens in front of the Observer studying the creation of universes from nothing. To Him, "nothing" is a pure space-time foam, without any classical space-time substrate.*

A question that could be asked is what happens to energy conservation. Well, as in the case of the Tryon universe, this universe is closed. The mass, which is positive energy, cancels itself out with the negative energy associated with the gravitational field. So the energy of our Universe is zero and there are no problems with energy conservation. Another question is: why should this event, the origin of the Universe, happen? Because, as mentioned, quantum mechanics allows everything that can happen, with a certain probability. So the laws of physics do not prohibit the Universe from appearing. Another way of seeing things, according to Wilczek, is that the Universe originates, because *"vacuum is unstable".*

At this point we need to make a couple of observations. In the first place, the Vilenkin scenario is not a certain and accepted fact by all scientists. It is a speculation in accordance with the physical laws. Secondly, assuming that Vilenkin's model is correct, the nothing we have spoken of is not "nothing", because in the description Vilenkin also refers to *"quantum foam".* The latter represents the structure of space-time generated by quantum fluctuations and is made up of micro-regions of space-time having dimensions equal to the Planck length. Furthermore, the nothing is not absolute "nothing" since the laws of physics are necessary for everything we have described to happen. At this point the problem arises whether the laws of physics arise with the birth of the Universe or whether they are external to it. Many great thinkers have always imagined that the reality that the senses show us is only the manifestation of a deeper reality. For example, in Plato's cave myth, prisoners held in a cave perceived what the outside world was only through its shadows. Underneath the apparent complexity of nature lies a kind of code written in mathematical terms: *natural laws.* For Galileo or Newton, laws were thoughts in the mind of God. This idea was also St. Augustine's point of view. Where are these laws found? According to Plato, mathematical objects had their own existence but were not part of the world we live in, but in the *"world of ideas".* Most modern physicists also believe that physical laws are real objects that transcend physical reality. Hence the problem of who established those laws? Life can be built by evolution, the laws of physics do not evolve and cannot develop from some simple initial core. So the question of where the laws of physics came from is a fundamental and unsolved problem. Another remarkable aspect is the fact that these laws are represented in mathematical form. According Roger Penrose the agreement between mathematics and physics request profound reasons and Eugene Wigner wrote:

> the enormous usefulness of mathematics in the natural sciences is something bordering on the mysterious and that there is no rational explanation for it:..it is an article of faith

The universe through these laws manifests itself as understandable to us. This rational intelligibility has led several scientists to think that the universe must be a product of intelligence.

In the latter case, even neglecting quantum foam, Vilenkin's model does not create a Universe out of nothing. In his bestseller *A Universe from Nothing*, Lawrence Krauss refers to Vilenkin's work to explain the birth of a universe from nothing. The conclusions Krauss reaches have no objective basis in current research. In fact, (excluding the Tryon model containing several incorrect points) the Vilenkin model does not generate a universe from nothing, since the nothing that Vilenkin talks about is not exactly "nothing", as discussed.

It should be noted that Vilenkin in his article talks about the limits of the approach:

> Most of the problems discussed in this article belong to "metaphysical cosmology", which is a branch of cosmology totally decoupled from observations. This does not mean, however, that such problems do not allow a rational analysis ....

Vilenkin, unlike Krauss, is very clear that his calculation is a simple model and that the birth of a universe from nothing is a much more complex problem. Theories based on quantum gravity do not say much more than other cosmologies with respect to the origin of the Universe. In the words of Tanu Padmanhaban

> *How (and why!) was the universe created and what happened before the big bang? The cosmologist who gives a lecture usually mumbles about the need for a quantum gravity model to circumvent the classical singularity, but we really have no idea! String theory offers no information; The implications of loop quantum gravity for quantum cosmology has recently attracted a fair amount of attention, but it's fair to say that we still don't know how (and why) the universe was born.*

The time is not yet ripe to have a clear idea of how the Universe could have been formed. You need to have a complete theory of quantum gravity, but even with this it is not clear if we may solve the problem.

## Summary: Keynotes

- There are various models of cyclical universes or universes in general that seem to have an infinite life and therefore lack a beginning. Vilenkin and Mithani studied three of these universes: the cyclical model of Steinhardt and Turok, eternal inflation and the so-called "emerging universe", showing that all three types of universe, although apparently without origin, have a beginning. In other words, all universes have a beginning and we must ask ourselves how they were born.
- Observational data tells us that our universe is flat, i.e. Euclidean, and this implies that its total gravitational energy is zero.
- Inflation transforms a tiny region of space into a macroscopic Universe without spending energy. The empty space is endowed with negative pressure which gives rise to antigravity which causes exponential expansion

and furthermore a space endowed with negative pressure expands and does not lose energy, rather it gains it. The total energy of the field that produces inflation will grow with expansion, while the total energy of the Universe will remain zero. The result is that the Universe is a *"free meal"*.

- The early universe is so small that it can be studied using quantum mechanics and taking gravity into account. Approximate calculations have found an equation similar to the Schrödinger equation for quantum cosmology, the Wheeler-de Witt equation. Its solution is the wave function of the universe.

- Using quantum cosmology and a particular initial state for the Universe, Vilenkin showed that the Universe can be generated from nothing, through quantum tunneling, where by nothing is meant the absence of space-time. However, this model is not a realistic model of the formation of the Universe from nothing, since the system that generates the Universe is not really nothing. For example, physical laws are present and the question arises as to who generated them. The existence of these laws and the intelligibility of the universe has led some thinkers to argue that it is a product of intelligence.

# CHAPTER 10

# WHAT DO WE KNOW ABOUT THE ORIGIN OF LIFE?

*Anyone who tells you that he or she knows how life started on earth some 3.4 billion years ago is a fool or a knave. Nobody knows*

— Stuart Kauffman

How did life begin? Where do we come from and who are we? These are the biggest questions we can ask ourselves and which certainly have always fascinated the human being. Giving an answer poses problems of formidable difficulty. A large number of scientists, in the last century, have attacked the problem from different angles, but no one has so far been able to solve it. Despite this, research has made significant progress and it is hoped in the future to be able to find a solution to the problem. From a general point of view, some answers can be given. The best known is that life was created by a deity. As we know, there are and have existed a large number of ideas on the origin of the world linked to divinities. In more recent times a more cryptic theory has appeared, the intelligent design that does not deny the reality of evolution, but argues that the extreme complexity of living beings can only be explained by the existence of an intelligence that has directed the evolution to follow the paths it has followed. The second, following the astrophysicist Fred Hoyle and his theory of the stationary universe, according to which the Universe is eternal, life would never have an origin, life would always exist. His collaborator Wickramasinghe also supported this thesis, and the idea that space was full of life (viruses, bacteria, etc.).

With the discovery that the *theory of the stationary universe* was wrong, the idea that life has always existed also decayed. A third possibility is that life did not originate on Earth, but that it came from space. This is the theory of *panspermia*. Proponents of this theory are Svante Arrhenius, Fred Hoyle, Francis Crick, among many. According to Crick there would have been too little time for a terrestrial origin of life and according to him it was more likely that an extraterrestrial civilization would have spread life everywhere. This is the hypothesis of *guided panspermia*. The idea of panspermia, of course, only moves the problem of the birth of life, from our planet to another place, but does not solve it. Panspermia is a scientific theory, but it is considered less likely than the local origin of life, that is, on Earth. Today we still don't know how things happened, but step by step we are getting closer to knowing how they could have happened. Despite the progress made in this area, the controversy still exists between the idea that life is the result of *chance*, according to the ideas of Jacques Monod, or of a *necessity* imposed by natural laws, as argued by Ilya Prigogine. The study of the origin of life is so complex that it requires interdisciplinary work. Nobel laureates in physics, chemistry and biology have dealt with and continue to deal with this complex and extraordinarily interesting problem.

## 10.1 The Earth at the Time of the Appearance of Life

As Aleksandr Ivanovich Oparin argued

> *The origin of life is an inalienable part of the general process of the development of the Universe and, in particular, of the development of the Earth*

For this it is necessary to discuss how the Earth evolved and the conditions present at the time that life made its appearance. Oparin imagined the conditions in which the Earth was at the formation: a very hot semi-molten surface, with a continuous fall of meteorites on it, and a wide range of chemical substances including those based on carbon (organic reactions). Then the Earth cooled and the water vapor condensed into liquid water, resulting in rain. Thus the oceans were formed, warm and rich in chemicals. These may have reacted by forming new compounds, in the direction of increasing complexity. Oparin thought that sugars and *amino acids* formed in the waters of the early Earth. The new chemicals began to form microscopic structures. Since some chemicals do not dissolve in water, coming into contact with it they could have formed spherical globules called *coacervates* of the order of 0.01 cm. The coacervates would have been the subject of selection that would have led to the origin of dynamic and stable systems. Oparin then proposed that coacervates were the ancestors of modern cells.

Returning to the conditions of the early Earth, we know that Earth, like any planet, is the result of star formation. The first stars appeared a few hundred million years after the Big Bang. The first stars were much larger than the present ones, some hundreds of solar masses, and they did not have planetary systems since they did not contain heavy elements, necessary for the formation of the planets. The heavier elements as shown in the famous article by Mr and Mrs Burbidge, Hoyle and Fowler. The primordial stars, given their large mass, have a short life and end their life by passing into the supernova phase, in whose explosion the heavy elements that have been built in the stellar interior are projected into space. These in turn can give rise to a second generation star system, which may already have planets made up of heavy elements. The relative abundance of heavy elements in our solar system suggests that it is a third generation system. Life therefore appeared only after second or third generation planetary systems appeared in the Universe. Estimates on the age of the Earth converge on about 4.5 billion years, using for example the dating of the most ancient meteorites. Our solar system, like the others, was formed from the collapse of a huge nebula of gas and dust. In the collapse phase, the conservation of the *angular momentum* (typical quantity of rotating bodies) increased the rotation speed of the system and gave rise to a disk structure, in which planets were subsequently formed.

The formation of the Earth occurred by agglomeration of the dust of the disk, which formed ever larger objects. These objects known as *planetesimals* by impact and accretion formed the *protoplanets*. In a period between ten and one hundred million years, a body the size of Mars (called *Theia*, name of Selene's mother, which indicates the name of the Moon) collided with the Earth. The great impact hurled a fraction of the mass of the Earth into space, forming a disk that over time gave rise to the Moon. The event was of considerable importance for the Earth, since our satellite stabilizes the oscillations of the earth's axis and consequently the seasons. At that time the Earth was melted and obviously could not host life. The period from the formation of the Earth up to about 4 billion years takes the name of the *Hadean eon* from the Greek term Hades, meaning hell, to indicate the infernal conditions existing on the planet at that time. The Earth cooled quickly, so much so that about 4.4 billion years ago, a crust probably already existed on which water began to accumulate. Under these conditions, life could theoretically have appeared, but if this happened it could not survive the *late bombardment*, a period of intense bombardment by meteorites and comets that occurred between 4.1 and 3.8 billion years ago. According to most scientists, life could have appeared and preserved only after 3.8 billion years ago, times in accordance with some fossil remains that we will discuss shortly. If this happened, life developed very rapidly, over a *period between 50 and 350 million years*. This would indicate that life is a probable process and that therefore extraterrestrial life should also be expected to exist. From an astronomical point of view, it is estimated that 3.9 billion years ago, the Sun must have emitted about 30% less radiation than it is today and that therefore the Earth should have been completely frozen, a sort of snowball (*snowball Earth*).

This seems to be in contradiction with the findings of *Isua*, which we will discuss about, which would testify the existence of liquid water. This contradiction could be overcome by thinking that at that time the atmosphere was such as to give rise to an intense *greenhouse effect*. It is therefore natural to ask what was the composition of the Earth's atmosphere at that time. There are several controversies about the composition of the Earth's atmosphere. Considering the most accredited ideas, we can say that the atmosphere was made up of *reducing gases*, namely gases that tend to acquire electrons in a reaction: *hydrogen* ($H_2$), helium (He), and to a lesser extent water ($H_2O$), methane ($CH_4$), ammonia ($NH_3$), nitrogen ($N_2$), etc. Due to the solar wind, the high temperature, and the meteoric impacts, the lighter gases (hydrogen and helium) were lost from the atmosphere. Methane and ammonia decreased due to solar radiation. The atmosphere was replaced by that coming from the bowels of the Earth due to the *Great Eruption*, i.e. the continuous emission of gas from volcanoes. As a consequence, the concentration of carbon dioxide ($CO_2$) increased, with a concentration from one hundred to a thousand times higher than the current one. The primeval Earth already had water on the surface, as we have already said. In addition to the water already present, more came thanks to comets from the *Kuiper belt* or the *Oort Cloud*. Together with the comets on Earth, asteroids also fell in numbers higher than the current one. This brought a large amount of water, to which was added that due to volcanic degassing. An observer would have had a very different vision from the current one, with a much larger Moon than the current one being at a distance of one third of the current one, and seas probably of brown-green color and a sky of red-orange color. The tides were much higher than they are today and the length of the day was almost half of the current one. An important question we need to ask ourselves is when did life appear on Earth. The oldest fossils are used to date the beginning. Until the mid-1950s, the fossils found served to date the *Cambrian period* (541 million years ago). For the previous periods there was no great information. After 1954 fossils were found from *Gunflint* (Canada) dating back to about 1.9 billion years ago. After these other fossils were found in *Isua* (Greenland) called *Isua spheres* with an age of about 3.8 billion years. William Schopf, a paleontologist, defined criteria for *biogenicity*. With these criteria the spheres of Isua were introduced into the category of unidentified, while others were discarded. The oldest fossils identified were those of *Marble Bar* (Australia) with an age of 3.5 billion years, identified as *cyanobacteria*. The latter are green bacteria because they use photosynthesis. The biogenicity of Schopf microfossils is not absolutely certain. As shown by Juan Manuel Garcia Ruiz, biological structures can be similar to *biomorphs*[1] of inorganic origin. So Schopf's structures are microfossils on which doubts arise, pseudo microfossils. Of particular importance are the structures known as *stromatolites* (from the Greek "covered with stone"). Stromatolites are generated by the action of microorganisms, in particular cyanobacteria. They have disparate shapes ranging from flat to column shapes, etc. More recently, in 2011, some remains were found by Brasier, near the structures identified by Schopf, which have a greater guarantee of being authentic and which date back to about 3.4 billion years ago. In addition to morphological fossils there are chemical ones. The oldest strata are those of Isua, dating back to 3.8 billion years ago. There are also those of *Akilia*, dating back to 3.85 billion years ago but on whose biogenicity there are considerable doubts. Ultimately, from the fossils we come to the conclusion that life on Earth must have already existed 3.4 billion years ago, and possibly even earlier (3.8 billion years).

## 10.2 The Primordial Soup

Giving a definition of life is not trivial and even less trivial to talk about its origin. Despite this, Darwin had his own ideas on the origin of life which he did not publish, but which he spoke about in his private correspondence. In a 1871 letter addressed to his friend Hooker, Darwin spoke of the origin of life starting from chemical processes powered by energy sources. In the letter he spoke of a "*small hot pond*" as a possible primordial soup in which the first living organisms would be formed. In his words

> *But if (and oh what a big if) we could conceive in some warm*
> *little pond with all sorts of ammonia and phosphoric salts, light,*

---

[1] Structures that resemble a single-celled organism.

*heat, electricity etcetera present, that a protein compound was*
*chemically formed, ready to undergo still more*

*complex changes [..]*

and a few years later, in 1882, writing to Daniel Mackintosh
he confirmed his belief that in the future his idea, and the
possibility of formation of life as described could be proved.

Only in the 1920s, the problem of the origin of life was taken
up by the Russian biochemist Alexandr Ivanovich Oparin and
the English geneticist John Haldane. Both conceived the idea
of *chemical evolution*, that is the idea that in the primordial
seas there was an *organic soup* which, increasing in complexity,
would lead to the formation of simple cells, the point of origin
of all living beings. Due to the poor development of analytical
chemistry for many years there were no developments, nor
experimental ideas to verify the ideas of Oparin and Haldane.
The English version of Oparin's second book was read by Harold
Urey, Nobel Prize for Chemistry in 1934. In a seminar held at
the University of Chicago on the origin of the solar system
and in particular on experiments for the formation of organic
compounds, he was present a recent graduate in Chemistry,
Stanley Lloyd Miller. Some time later Miller showed up in
Urey's studio proposing to carry out some experiments. Urey
agreed to do the experiments, but if in six months there were
no positive results, they would have changed Miller's thesis.
Together they built a device containing liquid water and gases:
hydrogen, ammonia, methane. This was the idea of that time
on the constitution of the earth's atmosphere. The water was

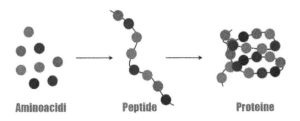

Aminoacidi      Peptide      Proteine

Figure 10.1.   Scheme: amino acids and proteins.

boiled in a pipette at the bottom, then cooled to form what was the rain in the primordial oceans. In the pipette at the top, electric discharges of very high voltage were produced, representing the lightning strikes of the early Earth. After a few days the water changed color, becoming reddish-brown. The analysis showed that various organic compounds had formed, including amino acids (*glycine* and *alanine*), which, as already mentioned, are the "building blocks" that form proteins.

The results of the experiment gave considerable support to the idea of *chemical evolution*. The experiment generated great expectations and gave a strong impetus to carry out other experiments. An important point to remember is the fact that the atmosphere used by Urey and Miller was a *reducing atmosphere*, while today it is thought that it should have been more *oxidizing*, that is, it tends to lose electrons in a reaction, containing $CO_2$, and water. Repeating the Urey-Miller experiment with an atmosphere of this type, the efficiency of the reaction is much lower, i.e. not all the substances of the Urey-Miller experiment were formed. Despite this error, the Urey-Miller experiment gave birth to *prebiotic chemistry*, stimulating the execution of a multitude of other experiments. Of considerable importance are the results obtained by the Spaniard Joan Orò. Until the late 1950s, the bases of nucleic acids[2] were not found, namely the chemicals *adenine (A), guanine (G), cytosine (C), thymine (T), and uracil (U)*. Figure 10.2a shows the localization of the bases in the RNA and DNA structure. In 1959 Orò conducted an experiment starting from hydrogen cyanide (HCN) obtaining a *nucleic acid base, adenine* (A), and together with Miller they found *guanine* (G), while all the other bases were found by other researchers. Thousands of early Earth simulation experiments were performed, using different forms of energy (ultraviolet radiation, visible, heat, radioactivity, electrical discharges) in different environments (aquatic, gaseous, atmosphere-water interface). Most of the

---

[2] Nucleic acids are macromolecules responsible for the storage and transport of genetic information, such as RNA and DNA (Figure 10.2). They consist of a sugar, a nitrogen base and some phosphate groups.

---

**INTERLUDE 3**

**NUCLEIC ACIDS, DNA AND RNA**

Nucleic acids (RNA; DNA) are macromolecules responsible for the conservation and transmission of genetic information. DNA has a *double helix* structure that resembles a ladder. RNA, on the other hand, has only one helix. The small segments connected to the helices are the *nitrogenous bases* (A, G, C, T, U). The helix is made up of *sugar phosphates*. The simplest units can form a chain of RNA or DNA are called *nucleotides* (see Figure 10.2b). Nucleotides are made up of a sugar called ribose, combined with a phosphate group from which an oxygen atom has been removed, and a base. The union of many nucleotides constitutes one chain (called *polynucleotide chain*), where the phosphate groups and sugars form the helix from which the nitrogenous bases protrude. The basics are matched according to a precise rule. In the case of DNA A is matched to T and C to G. So if a strand of the double helix begins with AGGTCCGTAATG .. the other will be TCCAGGCATTAC. That is, knowing one filament, the other can be deduced. The base sequence bears a message with this four-letter alphabet that conveys information for a protein. Plus each group of three nucleotide, called a *codon*, encodes an amino acid. Since there are four nucleotides, there are $4^3$ possible triplets available to encode the 20 amino acids. Genes are segments of DNA that contain the code for a specific protein. A complete set of genes makes up the *genome*. The human genome is 3.5 billion letters long. In the case of RNA G couples with C and A with U.

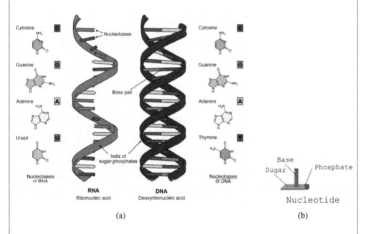

Figure 10.2.   (a) Nucleic Acids: RNA and DNA. (b) Nucleotide
https://it.wikipedia.org/wiki/Acidi_nucleici
https://www.my-personaltrainer.it/biologia/nucleotidi.html

*(Continued)*

*(Continued)*

**THE RNA WORLD**

The basic idea of the RNA world is that RNA chains could be generated on Earth. They would begin to replicate, be subject to Darwinian evolution, competing with each other for survival. The RNA chain is formed by the union of a certain number of nucleotides as in Figure 10.3a. As you can see, the atoms of the part made up of sugar phosphates (yellow part in Figure 10.3a and 10.2b) form strong bonds forming chains.

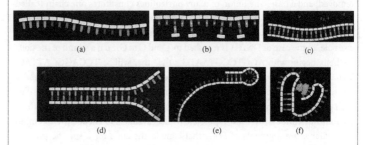

Figure 10.3.   (a) 17 nucleoid coupled to form a chain; (b)–(c) coupling between nucleotides; (d) separation of the two chains in hot water; (e) formation of the ribozyme; (f) reactions driven by ribozyme

To understand how RNA chains interact with the environment and can replicate, remember that the bases A, C, G and U couple in the following way: G couples with C, and A with U. With minimal help from the researchers, who form the chain from nucleotides, the RNA chains can replicate and evolve. If the chain is in a cold solution with high concentrations of nucleotides the nucleotides in solution bind to the chain as in Figure 10.3b and 10.3c. A complementary chain is thus formed to the starting one. By heating the water, the two chains separate as in Figure 10.3d, forming two separate chains ready to couple with other nucleotides. Normally with this procedure copies of the original chain are formed, but sometimes mutations can occur, due to writing errors of the nucleotide sequence. The selection that brings the chains to compete for survival comes into play. If in the cold solution the number of nucleotides is low, the RNA chain can fold back on itself giving rise to base coupling of the same chain as in Figure 10.3e and leaving some free bases facing outwards.

These bases can attract other molecules and give rise to chemical reactions as in figure 10.3f. A chain like this, capable of driving chemical reactions is called, *ribozyme*. The specific function of a ribozyme depends on its shape which in turn depends on the nucleotide sequence. Now suppose that a ribozyme has the ability

(*Continued*)

| INTERLUDE 4 |
| --- |
| **THE RNA WORLD** |
| to generate nucleotides from surrounding molecules. After many replicas, selection could hone this ability of ribozymes, as it gives them a greater chance to replicate. To see if this was possible, some researchers from Simon Fraser University have created a large number of RNA chains by analyzing their potential ability to produce nucleotides. Some chains were able to perform the operation and using a duplication technique by inserting random mutations ribozymes were obtained that produce nucleotides very efficiently. These molecules can actively participate in their survival, a typical feature of life. As mentioned, some intervention by researchers is still required to form the chains. Further studies are therefore needed. |

experiments highlighted the fundamental role of hydrogen cyanide and formaldehyde (HCOH). In 1969 the *Murchinson meteorite*, taking his name from the place where it was found and which is located in Australia, fell. It is a *carbonaceous chondrite* containing 14,000 different organic compounds, including 70 amino acids, but it is estimated that there could be millions. In addition to amino acids, the bases of nucleic acids were found. These substances are not due to contamination as evidenced by the presence of organic compounds not found on Earth. The composition is similar to that of the results of the Urey-Miller experiment. This finding is of considerable importance because it shows that, even if due to the low-reducing character of the earth's atmosphere, the *primordial soup* did not produce many compounds (as in the Urey-Miller experiment in a low-reducing environment). The contribution of extraterrestrial material could play a fundamental role in the birth of life. A few years ago, the study of comet *67 P/ Churymov-Gerasimenko* showed the existence of HCN, nitrogen compounds, aldehydes, and alcohols. So comets could also bring a certain amount of *probiotic molecules.*

## 10.3 From the Primordial Soup to LUCA

However, even assuming that chemical processes on Earth or in space could generate amino acids, sugars, nucleotides, etc., from these substances to the formation of life and the so-called *LUCA* (Last Universal Common Ancestor) there 'is a long way to go. A *metabolism* is needed for the functioning of the ancestral organism. *Metabolism* is the ability to extract energy from the surrounding medium and use it to stay alive. Metabolism is based on proteins that are fundamental in the life process, *enzymes*. These enzymes are synthesized starting from the information present in the nucleic acids. Unfortunately, for the nucleic acids to duplicate and express information, enzymes are needed. We are faced with the *problem of the chicken and the egg in the field of the origin of life*: enzymes are produced by nucleic acids, but for the latter to duplicate, enzymes are needed.

It would be necessary for the components of life to be formed all together and collaborate to generate it.

Leslie Orgel set out to simplify the problem and suggested that early life had no proteins or DNA. The engine of life was composed almost entirely of RNA. For this to work, the primordial RNA molecules had to be very versatile, and first they had to be able to make copies of themselves. The idea that life began with RNA proved to be very influential. RNA can do something that DNA, a rigid double-stranded structure (double helix) (see Figure 10.2) cannot. Being a single-stranded molecule it could fold into a variety of shapes (Figure 10.3), and those folds seemed similar to the way *proteins* that are long strands of amino acids, behaves.

Among proteins there are some special ones, enzymes, which can catalyze (accelerate) chemical reactions. A suspicion arose in Orgel's mind. If RNA could fold like a protein, it could possibly form enzymes. If this were true, RNA would be capable of storing information and at the same time *catalyzing* reactions, as enzymes do.

In 1982, Thomas Cech and in 1983 Sidney Altman showed that these ideas made sense, showing that some RNA have catalytic capabilities (such as enzymes) and that they can function as enzymes. Now the idea that life began with RNA looked promising. These RNAs with enzymatic properties are called *ribozymes* (see the box *Interlude 4*). In other words, a ribozyme is an RNA molecule capable of catalyzing a chemical reaction, similar to enzymes. The discovery has major implications for our discourse on the formation of life. In fact, it is no longer necessary that the proteins and the nucleic acids, that encode them, have formed simultaneously. This leads to the idea of the so-called *RNA world*, a term coined by Walter Gilbert. According to Gilbert, the first stage of evolution consisted of "*molecules of RNA that carry out the catalytic activities necessary to assemble themselves from a soup of nucleotides*". In this world, the RNAs would be able to do the important things for the formation of life, that is, to carry genetic information and function as catalysts for chemical reactions.

The RNA world is an elegant way of reproducing the complexity of life from scratch. Instead of relying on the simultaneous formation of large numbers of biological molecules from the primordial soup, some sort of "handyman molecule" could do the job of all of them. The RNA world is now accepted as clues have been found in its favor. The most important is that the key reaction in the production of proteins, based on the union of the amino acids that constitute them, is catalyzed by an RNA called *ribosomal RNA* (rRNA). This study was developed by Thomas Steitz.

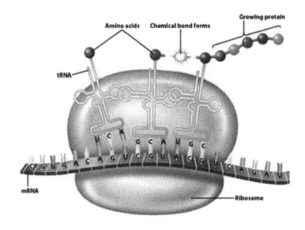

Figure 10.4.    Ribosome and translation of messenger RNA into proteins.

Each cell has a *ribosome*. It is a huge molecule that reads RNA instructions and combines amino acids to create proteins. The ribosome was known to contain RNA. In 2000, Steitz's team produced a detailed image of the ribosome structure, which showed that RNA is the catalytic core of the ribosome. The *messenger RNA* (mRNA) contains the information that is translated into the ribosome. The mRNA strand can be thought of as a magnetic tape while the ribosome as a kind of machine that builds a protein from the information on the tape (mRNA). To this end, the ribosome moves along the mRNA strand and as it passes it "reads" the information contained on the tape (mRNA). In the passage, the *codons* are read in the order in which they appear on the mRNA. Then the ribosome finds the amino acids corresponding to the codons. Amino acids are found near the ribosome, attached by particular bonds, called *ester bonds*, to molecules (called tRNA,[3] or transport RNA) that have the shape of crosses. After the ribosome has read a particular codon, it searches for the corresponding anticodon,[4] hooks it and removes the amino acid that is attached to it. The ribosome combines this amino acid with the others already put together, giving rise to the protein. So the discovery of the enzymatic capabilities of RNA implies that the RNA world had a complex metabolism. The organisms of this world would be subjected to evolution through natural selection. Although the existence of organisms capable of evolving is confirmed, there remain open points, such as the problem of the invention of the *genetic code* and the synthesis of proteins. Furthermore, the experiments are a long way from producing RNA. There remains the problem of how it could have formed on the early Earth. Gerald F. Joyce and Leslie Orgel argued that the

---

[3] The transport RNA (tRNA) connects and relates the information contained in 3 nucleotides (called codons) of the mRNA with the amino acids of the proteins. The tRNA reads the codons and supplies the amino acids corresponding to those letters.

[4] The anticodon is the base triplet present in the transport RNA (tRNA) with which the base triplet of the codon present in the messenger RNA (mRNA) is recognized. If the codon is made up of the AAC bases, the anticodon is UUG. Remember that G only mates with C and A only mates with U.

spontaneous appearance of RNA chains on early Earth *"would have been almost a miracle"*. Before talking about this aspect we would like to recall that the idea of Orgel and the RNA world were based on the idea that a fundamental aspect of life is its ability to reproduce itself. The idea put reproduction in the foreground. Indeed, other aspects are essential for life, such as metabolism. For many biologists, the defining feature of life is *metabolism* and in second place comes *reproduction*. This seems obvious enough, because before reproducing you have to be able to keep yourself alive. In the 1960s, scientists studying the origin of life split into two fields: those that polarized research on genetics and reproduction and those that put metabolism at the center. A third group argued that the first thing to appear was a container for key molecules, *cellularity* or *compartmentalization*. Compartmentalization for these researchers came first. In other words, a cell must exist. It is necessary that the vital material was enclosed by a membrane of fats and lipids. There are therefore three different research groups based on the different ideas enumerated.

The discovery of catalytic RNA led to the idea that it would account for at least two of the fundamental aspects of life: the genetic aspect and metabolism. There remains the problem of explaining how it appeared. As we have already said, Orò showed that nucleotide bases (A, G, ...) can be obtained in particular reactions, but the complex problem remains of how to generate an *RNA nucleotide* (called *ribonucleotide*) by connecting each base with sugar (known as *D-ribose*) which constitutes RNA, and this with a phosphate group (see Figure 10.2b). Sugar (D ribose) is formed in experiments, the source of phosphate could be *polyphosphates* present in volcanic emissions or meteoric phosphates. Despite the various attempts to obtain the necessary unions, it was not possible to carry them out. The other problem is that even managing to build nucleotides, it is then necessary to link them to form chains, *polymers*.

Furthermore, apart from the problem of RNA synthesis, its existence does not ensure the existence of an RNA world, since it must be able to replicate itself. There have been several attempts to replicate RNA in the absence of enzymes using two routes: without using enzymatic activity or using that of RNA. In the first case we start from some RNAs and nucleotides. British chemist Leslie Orgel tried this route for many years without success. Other researchers continued their work using chains of a few tens of nucleotides. Jack Szostak and Gerald Joyce are two of those who tried the second way: to use the enzymatic activities of RNA. In 2014 there was talk of a very efficient super replicator in vitro, but whose operation is unlikely in the primordial Earth. Several researchers continued to look for a way to replicate RNA. Despite all attempts, the problem has not been solved. The lack of a self-replicating RNA is a fatal problem for the idea of the RNA world. RNA does not seem to be able to start life.

When it was assumed that it was impossible to get from the primordial soup to the RNA, researches of John Sutherland's changed everything. Instead of trying to first form the sugar (D-ribose), phosphate and base and then combine them (see Figure 10.2b), he used *cyanide* derivatives and *aldehydes* in the presence of phosphate to obtain nucleotides of cytosine (C) and uracil (U). The research continued until it showed that HCN together with hydrogen sulfide, ultraviolet light and copper ions give rise to precursors of nucleotides, lipids and 11 amino acids. These discoveries brought closer to the solution of the egg and chicken problem mentioned, giving the idea that in some way egg and chicken could be formed and that the three essential characteristics of a minimal cell: *information (genetics)*, *metabolism* and *compartmentalization* could be carried out simultaneously.

## 10.4 Starting from the Metabolism

The RNA world theory is based on the idea that the most important thing for an organism is reproduction. However, there are many researchers who do not believe that reproduction is essential, since before reproducing, an organism must be self-sufficient. To stay alive it is necessary to absorb some form of energy. So they think the starting point is *metabolism*. As already mentioned, we call metabolism the ability to extract energy from the surrounding medium and use it to stay alive. This process is so important that many researchers think it is the first thing life has done. There is therefore a line of research that is based on the idea that metabolism comes first. What is the appearance of organisms that only have metabolism? One of the most interesting ideas is that of Günter Wächtershäuser of the late 1980s. For Wächtershäuser the first organisms were completely different from everything we know and were not made of cells, they would have been acellular, they had no enzymes, DNA or RNA. Both nucleic acids and information-carrying molecules were missing. However, they would have had a certain metabolism that developed in two dimensions and not in three, and a capacity for evolution. These compounds, like the terminal or intermediate products of metabolism (metabolites) were negatively charged, they were *anions*. Wächtershäuser imagined a flow of hot water, rich in volcanic gases such as ammonia and traces of volcanic minerals, which flowed from a volcano. Chemical reactions began to occur where the water flowed over the rocks. Metabolic cycles were created, that is, processes in which one chemical substance is converted into others, until the initial substance is recreated. In the process, the system absorbs energy used to start the cycle. These metabolic cycles did not resemble life. Wächtershäuser spoke of precursor organisms that could hardly be called living. He elaborated his model in the 80s–90s of the last century, in great detail, outlining which minerals were involved and the chemical cycles that took place. It was a theory that needed a discovery to support its ideas. This discovery had been made earlier in 1977 by a team led by Jack Corliss using a submarine near the Galapagos Islands. Corliss and collaborators observed volcanically active crests of rock rising from the sea. These ridges were covered with thermal springs. These areas were populated by a multitude of animals of different types. In other words, the scenario of this model and in which life was formed is that of underwater hydrothermal sources (hydrothermal chimneys known as *black fumaroles*) in the ocean floors.

In the model all organic compounds were formed in situ. We are faced with a self-sufficient metabolism, called

Figure 10.5.    Black fumaroles.

*autotrophic.* In the hypothesis of the primordial soup, on the contrary, the first living beings were *heterotrophic*, that is, they fed on it. The energy and "reducing power" required to transform CO and $CO_2$ into organic matter would be due to the reaction of formation of pyrite ($FeS_2$) starting from hydrogen sulphide ($H_2S$) from iron sulphide (FeS). The confirmation of this thesis came experimentally in 1990. After this, Wächtershäuser proposed a whole series of reactions that started with the assimilation of CO and $CO_2$ to end with the generation of cells. Furthermore, the current metabolic pathways would have been preceded by a series of reactions not catalyzed by enzymes. As a first step, we need to show how the incorporation of inorganic carbon takes place. According to the author, this was possible thanks to a $CO_2$-fixing auto-catalytic process. This cycle would promote the fixing of $CO_2$ into organic molecules. Wächtershäuser called his hypothesis the *world of iron-sulfur*. Stanley Miller argued that the hydrothermal vents were too hot, and the heat would destroy the chemicals produced, such as amino acids. Geologist Mike Russel found fossil evidence of thermal chimneys with temperatures below 150°C in the 1980s. Furthermore, the fossil remains of these vents contained pyrite, and he suggested that the first complex organic molecules were formed within the pyrite structures. Russel suggested that the thermal chimneys in the deep sea, warm enough to allow the formation of pyrite structures, housed the organisms of Wächtershäuser. According to this thesis, life began at the bottom of the sea and the metabolism appeared first. The idea was further modified based on a discovery by Peter Mitchell: the *Mitchell proton gradient.*[5] It was clear that a proton gradient is needed to store energy. Starting from this idea, Russel concluded that life is formed where there is a natural proton gradient. The ideal place would be a hydrothermal vent with water poor in protons, i.e. *alkaline water.* So acidic Corliss vents, as well as being too hot, wouldn't work for that. The first alkaline hydrothermal vents were discovered by Deborah Kelley in the Atlantic in a place called Lost City. The water temperature is between 40°C and 75°C and slightly alkaline. These vents were perfect for the ideas of Russell (who in the meantime began to collaborate with the biologist William Martin), who became convinced that in reality these were the places where life was born. The rocks of the vents are porous and formed sorts of pockets containing pyrite among the various chemical substances. In combination with the natural proton gradient from the air intake, these were the ideal places for the start of metabolism. After life had harnessed the chemical energy of the vent water, the production of molecules such as RNA began. With the formation of the membrane, a real cell is formed which then goes from the porous rock to the open sea.

Proponents of the RNA world have found two problems in the theory. The first problem is that there is no experimental evidence for the processes described by Russell and Martin. They expect results from experiments by Nick Lane who hopes to observe metabolic cycles and perhaps RNA as well. The second problem is the location of thermal vents in the deep sea and the fact that long-chain molecules such as RNA and proteins cannot form in the water without enzymes.

---

[5] The gradient indicates a difference in a given quantity between two positions.

In the last decade, a third approach has appeared that promises a way to create an entire cell from scratch.

## 10.5 Cells from the Start

In the RNA world, membranes were not taken into consideration although it is clear that it is unlikely that RNAs were found in solution without protection. In the Wächtershäuser hypothesis, the *membranes*, even if they appeared, did it very late. Researchers have realized that it is difficult to imagine life forms without membranes. It is clear, in current biology, that metabolism, genetics and cellularity are closely linked. Cellularity depends on membranes which are not mere semipermeable barriers, but also have important metabolic capabilities and are also essential for energy generation. Given the objective difficulty, the researchers chose to try to obtain the three characteristics mentioned separately. Given the failure of the approach, we arrived at the new trend of trying to obtain them at the same time, or at least to obtain two of the characteristics: cellularity and a second of the aforementioned characteristics. As already seen, Michael Russel emphasizes the importance of the iron-sulfur membranes formed in a not very hot and alkaline environment. We have also seen the importance of membranes in cell energetics and proton gradients. In today's cells, the membranes are made up of lipids and proteins. Lipids are the essential element to close the vesicles, because they are molecules that have a polar[6] and an apolar part. They can associate with each other and self-organize, through the apolar zones, placing the polar zones in the aqueous medium which is apolar. The membranes grow and the vesicles swell and at some point spontaneously divide.

In addition to the ease of formation and the ability to form microenvironments, vesicles can generate proton gradients, being a barrier between two apolar regions. As shown by

---

[6] Polarity is a property of molecules whereby a molecule has a partial positive charge on one side of the molecule and a partial negative charge on the opposite side of it.

Deamer in 2015, through hydration-rehydration cycles, the lipid vesicles give rise to the polymerization[7] of nucleotides. In rehydration, the RNAs are incorporated into the vesicles. Previous results have led several researchers to propose a *lipid world*[8] that would precede the RNA one. Jack Szostack set himself the goal of achieving RNA replication together with the growth and reproduction of vesicles, that is, an RNA cell capable of evolving. The latter story is linked to a collaboration between Szostack and the champion of the idea of "compartmentalization before", namely Pier Luigi Luisi. The latter's ideas can be traced back to those of the Oparin coacervates. Luisi's challenge was to create protocells, but despite various experiments he was unable to create anything truly realistic and convincing. In 1994 he suggested that the first protocells must contain RNA, which must be able to replicate inside the protocell. This idea quickly gained a supporter: Jack Szostak. The latter, in 2001, achieved great success. He added small amounts of a kind of clay called montmorillonite to his experiments and this accelerated the speed of vesicle creation by a factor of 100. Furthermore the latter absorbed the RNA filaments from the clay surface. The following year, Szostak's team discovered that protocells could grow on their own. Was it possible that they could also reproduce themselves? In 2009, Szostak and his student Ting Zhu made protocells with several concentric walls. By supplying fatty acids they grew and took a thread-like shape. A slight shear force allowed the protocell to be shattered into dozens of daughter protocells that contained the RNA of the parent protocell. There remained one thing to do: have the RNA replicate. Orgel had spent much of the 70s and 80s of the last century studying how RNA strands were copied. To do this, one needs to use a single strand of RNA together with loose nucleotides. Nucleotides are used to

---

[7] The term polymerization indicates the reaction whereby several molecules of the same low molecular weight compound (monomer) join together to form a plural molecule (polymer) with a higher molecular weight.
[8] Substances present in cells and in animal and plant tissues, characterized by insolubility in water and solubility in organic solvents.

assemble a second strand of RNA, complementary to the first. Orgel found that, under certain circumstances, RNA strands could copy without any help from enzymes. This may have been how early life made copies of his genes. Already in 1987, Orgel starting from a 14 nucleotide long RNA strand was able to create complementary strands of 14 nucleotides. Szostak and his student, Kataryna Adamala, tried to carry out this reaction in the protocells. To do this they needed magnesium, but this damaged cells. The problem could be solved with citrate (a substance almost identical to the citric acid found in citrus fruits). In a 2013 study, they saw that citrate bound to magnesium protecting the cells while allowing the model copy to continue. They had managed to implement Luisi's proposal, to perform RNA replication within the fatty acid vesicles. Szostak's team has managed to build protocells that retain their genes and at the same time absorb molecules from the outside. The protocells can grow, divide and the RNA can replicate inside. These results and those of Sutherland, already mentioned, suggest a new unified approach at the origin of life, based on all three functions, which we have indicated several times, can be achieved simultaneously.

In conclusion, the previous discussions highlight the great difficulties in finding a way that explains how life appeared on Earth. The times required for the emergence and subsequent evolution of life based only on random processes are prohibitive as we will see in the next chapter. As Francis Crick said, with the knowledge at our disposal we are led to think that the origin of life is a miracle. Several scientists think that some form of intelligence is needed to get the process started.

## Summary: Keynotes

- There are two hypotheses on the origin of life. The first assumes that it originated on Earth a few hundred million years after the formation of the Earth. The other hypothesis is that it was brought to Earth by comets or the like (panspermia).

- Fossils tell us that life must already exist on Earth between 3.4 and 3.8 billion years ago.
- Excluding panspermia, there are several theories on the origin of life. Darwin thought it formed in "a small hot pond" and some 2012 studies by Mulkidjanian and collaborators confirm this thesis. But this idea is contrasted, for example, by another which is based on the idea that life was formed in the depths of the oceans.
- Three aspects are fundamental for a living organism: reproduction, metabolism and cellularity. According to the RNA world hypothesis, the most important aspect of the three is reproduction, that is, genetics. The first entities capable of reproducing and evolving could be the RNA chains. In this hypothesis, the fundamental role in the generation of life on our planet would be due precisely to RNA. However, the model has various problems such as, for example, the formation of RNA starting from simple nucleotides in the primordial Earth.
- According to other scientists, metabolism is the starting point. Life would form in the oceans at underwater hydrothermal sources. The formation model is called the iron-sulfur world, due to the importance that these substances covered.
- A third possibility is that cellularity is the starting point. For example, in the lipid world the first self-replicating units were compounds similar to lipids, which in water form double layers, structures similar to those of today's cells.
- None of the models, however, can explain how life on Earth was formed. The problem still remains open. The problem of the origin of life is so complex that scientists speak of a "miracle".

CHAPTER 11

# ORIGIN AND EVOLUTION OF LIFE: CASE OR PROJECT?

*Natural selection was the main cause,
but not the only one, of the changes.*

— Charles Darwin

*It is grindingly, creakingly, crashingly
obvious that if Darwinism were really a
theory of chance, it couldn't work*

— Richard Dawkins

From the arguments deriving from physics and cosmology we have seen that there is no evidence that science has eliminated God. Among other sciences, biology is the one in which a number of thinkers argue that it is the science that best of all highlights the unnecessary existence of God. It is necessary to discuss whether the previous affirmation corresponds to the truth.

## 11.1 Order and Life

Understanding the origin of life is a puzzle of extreme difficulty. In half a century, several steps forward have been made in its solution. Today we know many mechanisms that some decade ago were even difficult to imagine, we know where we come from better than several decades ago, but we certainly haven't reached the goal of understanding how life formed.

Despite the thousands of experiments and decades spent trying to reproduce the formation of life in the primordial Earth, up to now this has not been successful. Amino acids, nucleotides were obtained, and theoretically in the laboratory the macromolecules at the basis of life could be created, but in practice we have not clarified the origin of life on Earth. Life is made up of long chains of amino acids, nucleic acids, and so on, but these chains are ordered. The sequences of amino acids and nucleotides that follow a precise order. If we use all twenty amino acids to form a chain of 50 amino acids organized in a random manner, we can obtain an enormous number of chains, almost as many as all the atoms in the universe, all different from each other. Unlike this situation, life is based on order and more precisely, as we will see, on the order linked to information.

For example, proteins are long chains with a precise order of amino acids. The same order dominates in genes and nucleic acids. The question that arises spontaneously is to ask how this order was established. If we knew we would have already solved our puzzle. The typical order of life can lead us on two different paths. That of the religious who supposes that there is an entity that has infused rules into the matter that push it to move towards order. Namely, an organizing being would move matter from states of greater disorder to the order necessary for life to be formed. The other path is that of science and today it tells us, in the voice of some of its exponents, such as Ilya Prigogine, that the appearance of living organisms is not an accidental event, but is implicit in the irreversible processes of systems far from equilibrium. There is a relationship between spontaneous *self-organization processes* and the birth of life. It is as if there is a kind of necessity in the world of non-life that pushes it in the direction of the living. Disorder is not the rule for matter, but only an intermediate stage that moves in the direction of creating an ever lower disorder until order is reached. Prigogine's ideas are based on his invention, *dissipative structures*, which is a thermodynamically open system that exchanges energy, matter and entropy with the environment and which is far from equilibrium.

Open systems with *autocatalysis*,[1] moving away from equilibrium, amplify small fluctuations and as a final result they self-organize, while dissipating entropy. In the book *The New Alliance* Prigogine and Isabelle Stengers give an example of how "the instability of a steady state gives rise to a phenomenon of spontaneous self-organization". It is the instability of Bènard. A liquid is placed in a container and the lower surface of the horizontal liquid layer is heated and brought to a higher temperature than that of the upper layer. A flow is generated from the bottom up and when the gradient exceeds a threshold value the fluid becomes unstable. A complex structure is generated, consisting of hexagonal structures, on the upper surface. A similar thing happens in dissipative structures. While in the Bènard cell instability has a mechanical origin and the behavior of the fluid flow is predictable in chemical systems, the situation is different. As the two authors report

> *The fate of the fluctuations that perturb a chemical system, like the regime of the new situations towards which it can evolve, depends on the detailed mechanism of the chemical reactions. Contrary to near equilibrium situations, the behavior of a far from equilibrium system becomes highly specific. There are no longer any universally valid laws from which the general behavior of the system could be deduced for any value of the boundary conditions. Each system is a case in itself, each set of chemical reactions must be explored and can produce a qualitatively different behavior*

Dissipative structures constitute a source to explain life not as an epiphenomenon due to chance, but which arises from the same laws of nature and matter, without excluding chance. There is a kind of plot that connects the non-living with the living. Matter is structured to become living matter.

---

[1] Autocatalysis is a catalytic process in which the catalyst is represented by one of the same reaction products or intermediates.

There is an order under the chaos, which led Prigogine to say

> *Each molecule knows what other molecules will do simulta-*
> *neously with it and at macroscopic distances ...... the mol-*
> *ecules communicate... [This property] in non-living systems*
> *comes at least unexpected.*

Like religion, Prigogine's science also leads us to the conclusion that there is a tendency of matter to always organize itself towards stages of a higher order, even to the point of giving birth to life. Without this tendency towards order it would be difficult to explain the formation of life in a reasonable time. For example, the formation of a single RNA molecule starting from nucleotides, randomly, would take much longer than the age of the universe. However, as we will see later, several scientists believe that Prigogine's self-organization is actually not sufficient to explain the transition from the non-living to the living.

The complexity of the origin of life without an underlying order led Francis Crick to conclude that it belongs to the realm of miracle

> *The origin of life appears to be almost a miracle, so many are*
> *the conditions which would have had to be satisfied to get it*
> *going*

So, the problem of the origin of life is so complex that scientists speak of a miracle. This is completely unexpected and leads us to ask ourselves if it is a mere expression to convey the idea of complicity or if the religious sphere is really brought into play. We have already mentioned Freeman Dyson who said

> *The more I examine the universe and the details of its archi-*
> *tecture, the more evidence I find that the universe in some*
> *sense must have known we were coming*

A third possibility to explain life, besides the religious and the scientific ones, which in this case seem to join hands, is that in reality we have understood very little of the formation of life and that many other efforts are to be made before a glimmer of truth enlighten us. It could be that things are much simpler than what we humans can conceive with our limited mind. This possibility seems to point to the fact that life, as already mentioned, took a short time (at most a few hundred million years) to begin. However, it could also be that the short time necessary for life to appear is due to the fact that it originated elsewhere and arrived on Earth ready to develop. Obviously this does not solve the problem of the origin of life but moves it to another place unknown to us.

## 11.2  Evolution and God

What reported about the Universe has highlighted that it is finely regulated and built to host life, and if you want to eliminate the idea of a project it is necessary to make bizarre hypotheses such as that of the existence of the multiverse. At the same time, the universe with its laws presents itself as intelligible and this is another reason that leads us to think that its origin is linked to a form of intelligence. Biology also seems to give the same indication.

John Lennox in his text *God's undertaker* makes a great effort to show that in biology, and in evolution, chance is not enough. In this and the following section we will follow some of his arguments.

Even biologists admit that the world was generated according to a project, but add that this is only an appearance. One of the best known atheistic biologists, Richard Dawkins, on the one hand argues that living beings give the impression of being designed, on the other writes, referring to the thesis of the clock and the watchmaker of Paley

> *the only watchmaker in nature is the blind forces of phys-*
> *ics, albeit deployed in a very special way. A true watchmaker*

*has foresight: he designs his cogs and springs, and plans their interconnections, with a future purpose in his mind's eye. Natural selection [...] has no purpose in mind. [...] It has no vision, no foresight, no sight at all. If it can be said to play the role of watchmaker in nature, it is the* blind *watchmaker.*

Crick and Watson take care to remind biologists that "*Biologists must constantly keep* in *mind* that what *they see* was *not designed, but rather evolved*".

There is no need for any project because evolution, which has nothing to do with intelligence, can produce all the complexity we see in the world.

Paley's argument is completely rejected. Indeed, it had already been attacked by David Hume in his *Dialogues on Natural Religion* and denied several times by various thinkers.

However, these claims clash with the simple arguments we will discuss in the next paragraph which highlight that chance alone cannot produce life.

At Darwin's Centenary (1959) Julian Huxley argued

*In the evolutionary pattern of thought, there is neither need nor room for the supernatural. The earth was not created; it evolved. So did all the animals and plants that inhabit it, including our human selves, mind and soul as well as brain and body. So did religion.*

It could be argued that God and evolution could coexist. God could have given rise to species that exist and have existed on Earth not directly, but by using evolution as a means or by using another argument, as John Houghton was thinking, we cannot exclude the idea of a designer just because we understand some of the mechanisms of the functioning of the universe or living systems. The idea that evolution leads to atheism as a logical consequence is therefore not accepted by all biologists, indeed there are many illustrious evolutionary biologists who are believers. Evolution is considered by most biologists and not only as an undeniable theory, such as the theory of gravitation. Is this exactly so? Discussing physics and cosmology, we saw that there are many points not clear, even if this is not usually stressed. Scientists speak about the multiverse, the origin out of nothing of the Universe as it were verified and certain ideas. In reality they are not. The devil is in the details. Now, discussing with main stream physicists or cosmologists, one can reach an equilibrium point in the discussion, and even heard from the counterpart that some ideas are speculative. This does not happen with biologists which are very rigid in their claims. Probably this is due to the fight biologists had with religions to impose the idea of evolution, for long time not accepted by religions. In any case, as physics, and cosmology have limits, evolutionary biology ideas are not 100% proved by fossils. In other words, biology is not a perfect science as biologist want us to think.

As we did in the case of physics and cosmology, we will now ask ourselves if evolution can do everything it promises to do or if it has limits. Before starting it must be remembered that the term "evolution" is used with different meanings. From a general point of view, the term evolution means the continuous accumulation of successive modifications, until morphological, structural, and functional changes occur in living beings. The times on which evolution works are the longer the greater are the changes to which it refers. Evolution therefore refers both to the ability to allow adaptation, to the ability to produce the appearance of given DNA sequences, to the ability to generate new species. You can therefore find different terms that refer to evolution. *Microevolution* indicates variations of existing structures, for example the way in which bacteria develop resistance to antibiotics. *Macroevolution* means an important change such as the appearance of a new organ and it implies an increase in complexity. *Molecular evolution* is used to describe the appearance of living material, such as cells, from non-living material. With regard to macroevolution and microevolution, the two previous terms are used to distinguish the evolution below and above the species level. According to the point of view of the *"gradualists"*, macroevolution must be the result of micro-evolutionary processes that operate for long periods. While the variations related to microevolution have been observed, it is more complicated to observe those of macroevolution as noticed by Paul Wesson. Now in the biologist community there are some scientists who do not completely agree with the dominant ideas. For example, Pierre Grassè of the Sorbonne was convinced, after much research, that there is a limit to what mutations and natural selection can do. In his text *Lévolution du vivant* (The evolution of the living) he highlighted that fruit flies after thousands of generations bred remain identical. There would seem to be a maximum evolution point and this suggests that natural selection will arrive at even lower results. Therefore, according to Grassè, microevolution does not maintain what one would expect from it. These ideas are obviously criticized by "orthodox" biologists. Studies on Escherichia Coli seem to confirm these conclusions. Biochemist Michael Behe highlights that in 30 thousand generations of Escherichia Coli which corresponds to about a million human years, the result is that evolution has produced *"involution, .... the bacterium has thrown away traits of the genetic heritage ... Nothing has been built having an elegance. It is easier to evolution demolish the things that build them."* This observation is considered by Behe as proof of the limit of evolution. Behe himself has argued that the best test of Darwinian theory is the history of malaria. According to him, "guided mutations" would be needed. These ideas and others have been rejected by orthodox biologists. We also cannot accept Behe's ideas which are strongly connected to the "intelligent design". However, there are critics to evolution from other scientists like the astrophysicist Fred Hoyle. He intervenes in the discussion by making calculations that led him to have doubts about the validity of extrapolation from micro to macroevolution. He wrote *"as common sense would suggest, Darwinian theory is correct in the small but not in the large"*. Another problem is related to fossils. Wesson and collaborators have argued that the fossil record does not give good examples of macroevolution. Darwin himself discussed the fossil problem. In the Origin of Species. He was writing that there should be a very large number of transitional, and intermediate varities (species), and was wondering why geology has not revealed this chain. He recognized that this point would be the most serious objection to his theory.

Has the situation changed today? It seems there is no change. Palentologist David Raup writes that after more than a hundred years since Darwin, knowledge of fossils is greatly expanded, but the situation we were talking about has not changed much, and that the the evidence in favor of evolution is very fragmented. Ironically, nowadays there are fewer examples of evolutionary transition than in Darwin's time.

According to Stephen Jay Gould there are features not consistent with the idea that fossils evolved gradually. These are 1. sudden appearance, and 2. stasis, namely the fact that almost all species do not show any directional change during their stay on Earth.

These observations led Gould and Eldredge to develop their own theory called *"punctuated equilibrium"*. Gould also highlighted how the taxonomic categories (phyla) present on Earth today appeared in the *Cambrian period* (which started 541 million years ago), the so-called *Cambrian explosion*. There are more moderate opinions than those of Gould, such as that of Simon Conway Morris, which in any case confirms the Cambrian explosion. Obviously, the theory of punctuated equilibrium is in stark contrast to the ideas of neo-Darwinists such as that of Dennet or Dawkins. These have a gradualist view of evolution, that is, that the small changes of microevolution add up to give rise to macroevolution. It is argued that the evidence cannot fail to be incomplete, especially for the soft parts of the body that do not fossilize easily. Palentologists know this problem well and despite it think that the lack of fossils does not solve the problems mentioned above. According to James Valentine, many of the branches of the tree of life cannot be traced back to precise ancestors and although the incompleteness of the fossils plays a part in complicating matters, it cannot be the only reason why they cannot be traced back to precise ancestors. In addition, there are sponge embryos preserved and found in China. So if soft embryos have managed to preserve themselves it is not clear how there are no remains of the precursors of Cambrian animals. It seems that fossils do not give Darwinian theory, at the level of macroevolution, the claimed and hoped support. Evidence against the idea that evolution has a limit comes from the studies of molecular biology. By comparing the structures of the DNA sequences in a series of organisms, it was highlighted that there is an extraordinary correspondence between the genomes, and the stretches of DNA that appear identical in different organisms.

These researches, independent of fossil remains and comparative anatomy, are considered as certain proofs of the genetic relationship between all living beings and would be the overwhelming proof of neo-Darwinian ideas. These studies prove a genetic kinship between living beings, but obviously stating that there is genetic kinship is not the same as saying that mutations and selection are the only propellants that push this kinship. The similarities present in the DNA sequences could be interpreted in different ways, even as evidence of a common project.

So we can ask ourselves whether evolution actually eliminates the need for a project. For Dawkins and many other biologists, the mechanisms of evolution explain the apparent design of the universe. You cannot have a project, a Creator and at the same time evolution. That is, evolution implies atheism. Is this idea shared by all biologists? No, it is not. There are several biologists who accept the idea that evolution can explain all the complexity of life but do not believe that it is incompatible with the existence of a project. As we have already said, in the words of John Houghton, understanding a part of how living beings work does not imply that there should not be a designer. Finally, the absoluteness of the conception of some biologists is not understood: either God or evolution. Isn't it possible that the designer intervened in the planning phase of the laws and then let these laws take their course?

## 11.3 The Difficult Road to Life: Chance is not Enough

In chapter 10 and in the previous section we have seen the problems in explaining the origin of life. According to geneticist Michael Denton, passing from the non-living to the living world a huge leap is made. Somehow the most fundamental and dramatic of the discontinuities of nature.

To understand the objective difficulties, let's try to do some calculations to see for example what the problems are in explaining the origin of proteins and complex systems containing information.

In living structures, proteins that are made up of amino acids play a fundamental role. We have seen that in the Miller and Urey experiment amino acids can be formed in a simple way in unguided processes. However, we also said that the constitution of the earth's atmosphere was different from that of the experiment mentioned above and in the real earth's atmosphere the formation of amino acids is problematic. Assuming we have amino acids, making a protein is by no means simple. If we want to build a protein containing 100 amino acids we must remember that they exist in two chiral forms. The term "chiral" comes from the Greek "hand". If we reflect the right hand in a mirror it will appear to us as if it were the left and vice versa. In general, in chemistry a molecule is called chiral if it cannot be superimposed on its mirror image. So a molecule can have two forms which are called L (from left-handed) and D (from right-handed).

In prebiotic simulation experiments they appear in equal numbers and therefore the probability of having one of the two forms is ½. The proteins present in nature are of the L form. Therefore the probability of obtaining 100 amino acids of the L form is given by $(1/2)^{100}$ that is one probability in $10^{30}$. To form proteins, amino acids must unite. The bonds to form proteins must all be the same. These bonds are called *peptide bonds*. In the experiments the number of peptide bonds is no more than half. The probability of a peptide bond is ½ and the probability of having 100 bonds of this type of bonds is 1 in $10^{30}$. Thus the probability of having 100 L-type amino acids with peptide bonds is 1 in $10^{60}$. The formation of peptide chains of amino acids has enormous thermodynamic problems. As Paul Davies reported, in order to form a short polypeptide could be formed, it is necessary a concentrated solution of amino acids with a volume large as the visible Universe.

To this problem is added another problem. Life emerged a few hundred million years after the origin of the earth and this time is not enough for the random mixing of molecules. The biggest problem we have is how proteins are formed from amino acids. A protein is not obtained by simply mixing amino acids, in the right proportions. Protein can be thought of as a "word" made up of letters, i.e. amino acids. The order in which the amino acids are placed in the chain is fundamental. For a "word" (protein) to make sense, the "letters" (amino acids) must be placed in the right position. Twenty amino acids are involved in the production of proteins. Considering a set made up of all 20 amino acids, the probability that a given amino acid is found in a certain point of the protein is 1/20. If we extend the calculation to 100 amino acids, the probability of obtaining 100 amino acids in the right order is $(1/20)^{100}$, or 1 in $10^{130}$. This calculation concerns a single protein but life requires hundreds of thousands of proteins. The probability of producing them by chance is less than 1 in $10^{40000}$. In other words, with blind randomness you can't even build proteins, and even less life. As indicated in the previous section, a possible solution proposed is that of *self-organization*, studied by Prigogine. He had shown how structures such as the Benard cells, typical of the Raylegh-Benard convection, could be formed. Another example of the formation of ordered structures from the disorder is that of the Belousov-Zhabotinsky reaction in which malonic acid, potassium bromate and two catalysts are mixed, keeping the mixture at 25°C a continuous change of color between red and blue is observed at intervals about a minute. According to some, life could have arisen in self-organizing systems such as these.

According to Robert Shapiro, the origin of life occurred in a scenario, which we described in the previous chapter, in which the metabolism is born first and in it we have the genesis of a *"type of life ... defined as the creation of a greater order in regions localized through chemical cycles fed by a flow of energy"*. Leslie Orgel provides an assessment of such cycles by arguing that their existence is implausible. Even if such cycles had existed, the idea that they could give to life clashes with the great difficulties related to the structure of proteins. The problem is not that of introducing order as in self-organizational processes, but a type of organization similar to that of language. As reported by Paul Davies, life is not a sort of self-organization, but a specified organization genetically directed. Thousands of experiments have been carried out since Miller and Urey's first experiment, but no great progress has been made in the field of studying the origin of life on Earth. In the words of Klaus Dose, expert in the field of the origin of life: "*More than 30 years of experimentation on the origin of life in the fields of chemical and molecular evolution have led to a better perception of the immensity of the problem of the origin of life on Earth rather than to its solution. At present all discussions on principal theories and experiments in the field either end in stalemate or in a confession of ignorance*".

These conclusions are echoed by Francis Crick, Stuart Kauffman, and Francis Collins. To understand even more the difficulties related to the difficulties that life implies, one must move even lower from the level of proteins to that of the fundamental building block of life, DNA. A living cell is matter containing an immense amount of information located in DNA. The cell has similar characteristics to computers, but with much more advanced information processing capabilities. It is not difficult to understand why studies on the origin of life get stuck on the question of how the genetic code and the mechanisms of translation originated. Among other things, it seems that this system has not undergone changes for billions of years. Werner Lowenstein stress that in genetic lexicon nothing has changed in two billion years, and that all life forms from bacteria to humans the same 64-word code.

According to Richard Dawkins, the origin of biological information can be explained by random, unguided natural processes. In one of his texts, *The Blind Watchmaker*, he uses an analogy already used in the past, that of typist monkeys who, having enough time, could compose any text by typing at random. As we have already discussed, this argument could only work if infinity were included in the argument, that is, the time available to monkeys is infinite. It can be shown using mathematics that the idea of typing monkeys does not hold up. For example, Russel Grigg estimated that to compose a text of 603 characters (including numbers, letters and spaces) and if the monkey presses a key per second, it takes a time of the order of $10^{1017}$ years, vastly greater than the age of the universe of 13.8 billion years. A simulator has even been created, simulating 100 monkeys each pressing a key every second. The simulator doubled the number of monkeys at regular intervals of two or three days. The experiment went on until 2007 when the "*Monkey Shakespeare simulator Project*" website stopped updates. In January 2005, after $2.7 \times 10^{39}$ monkey years of random typing, 24 characters were reached, corresponding to 24 letters of Henry IV, part two.

This type of calculations makes it clear that random processes cannot explain the origin of complex systems that contain information. Another example is that of hemoglobin. Isaac Asimov calculated the probability of obtaining a hemoglobin molecule from amino acids. The molecule is made up of four amino acid chains. Each chain is made up of 146 amino acids and the number of amino acids in living beings is 20. There are $20^{146}$ ($10^{190}$) ways of arranging the 20 amino acids in a chain of 146 links. Richard Dawkins himself, one of the best known neo-Darwinists, realizes that life is not built with chance. He wrote

> *It is grindingly, creakingly, crashingly obvious that if Darwinism were really a theory of chance, it couldn't work,*

in agreement with so many other scientists such as Hoyle and Wickramasinghe who argue that

> *The likelihood of the formation of life from inanimate matter is 1 to a number with 40,000 noughts after it ($10^{40,000}$).... It is big enough to bury Darwin and the whole theory of evolution.*

The problem arises of how to explain the origin of complexity. Richard Dawkins' idea, in his text *Climbing mount improbable*, is *by breaking the improbability up into small, manageable parts, smearing out the luck needed, going round the back of Mount Improbable and crawling up the gentle slopes inch by million-year inch*

In other words, invoking chance to explain the emergence of a vital form is equivalent to climbing Mount Improbable from the steepest side. The slow and cumulative variations, given by the accumulation of natural selection processes, correspond to the most docile paths. It is evident with simple calculations such as those shown above that evolution cannot be based on chance. For this reason, even Richard Dawkins, in his book *The Blind Watchmaker*, states that evolution was not a completely random process.

It is clear that there is a problem in Dawkins argument. From one side Dawkins, and the neodarwinists claim that *the only watchmaker in nature is the blind forces of physics* and from the other *that if Darwinism were really a theory of chance, it couldn't work*. These argument are in clear contradiction. According to the first claim, evolution is a blind process, and according to the second, blind processes cannot create all the variety of species present in our planet. Therefore, we should conclude that evolution is not a process capable of operating the "miracle" of creating the terrestrial biosphere. Dawkins does not appear to have realized this logical contradiction in his argument. Most likely he did not realize it since elsewhere he was discussing how the problem of the "causality" of evolutionary processes can be solved.

Dawkins thinks of solving the problem with a sort of *"cumulative selection"* system, in which the improvements made at each small step are verified, discarding the less efficient solutions. According to Dawkins, this introduces law-like behavior. The author has even developed a computer program that creates and modifies branched two-dimensional structures in order to simulate biological processes. These *"biomorphs"*[2] selected according to logics created by the

---

[2] A biomorph is a figure obtained on the computer using an algorithm and which is similar to a single-celled organism.

author (not through natural selection) are able to recreate complex shapes in a limited number of steps. From this Dawkins comes to the conclusion that the only viable way for evolution is to operate with small and gradual steps allowing it to create complex structures in a limited time. Non-gradual jumps would not exploit the idea (invented by Dawkins) of *cumulative selection*, making changes unlikely. Recall that this idea of evolution is an idea of Dawkins designed to reduce the steps necessary to reach a certain goal. The other fundamental point is that Dawkins introduces a verification at every certain number of steps and obviously, the idea of verification implies the introduction of something that has a certain intelligence and this is contrary to Dawkins' own statements that evolution is blind and without purpose. To get an idea of how much the processes are accelerated with Dawkins' assumptions, just follow his argument. In the first place, referring to the "typing monkeys", instead of considering the entire work of Shakespeare, he considers a reference phrase, a *target phrase*.

He chooses, a sentence from Hamlet[3] consisting of 28 letters, counting spaces as letters, and it should be obtained from 28 monkeys typing on the keyboard. By typing randomly, the probability of getting all the letters in one attempt is 1 in $27^{28}$, or 1 in $10^{40}$. To improve the situation Dawkins introduces a change. Now when the monkey presses the key, it compares the letter produced with the target letter in the sentence. If the letter obtained is the target letter, the letter is kept and the monkey stops writing. In this way, the target sentence is obtained in just 43 attempts! The difference between the casual situation and the second is abysmal. However, as mentioned earlier, we should be wondering who will carry out the verification? Some form of intelligence is needed and this is in contradiction with the idea of a blind and purposeless evolution. Dawkins introduces two mechanisms (a comparison mechanism between each attempt and the target sentence and another mechanism that preserves each successful attempt) that involve an intelligent mind. Ultimately, Dawkins's exercise

---

[3] The sentence is "Methinks it is like a weasel".

highlights, as Lennox points out in *God's undertaker,* that *"sufficiently complex systems such as languages of any kind, including the genetic code of DNA, cannot be explained without prior injection into the system of the information looked for".* Random processes have great problems even in explaining how a protein is formed from amino acids and the existence of information in cells further complicates the situation. To get out of the impasse, it is plausible to think that life has somehow been guided in its appearance.

## Summary: Keynotes

- Even in biology as in physics and cosmology the world seems to have originated following a precise project. Biologists admit this, but at the same time claim that it is only appearance. In reality, evolution, a blind and aimless process, can explain the forms of life we observe.
- There are actually unclear points. The fossils do not give evidence of a slow and continuous evolution, there seem to be leaps and most of the species appeared in the Cambrian explosion. Molecular biology has highlighted that there is a kinship between all species, but this does not imply that the origin of this kinship must be due to random mutations and natural selection.
- Simple calculations show that chance is not enough to push evolution forward. The likelihood of protein formation from amino acids is very small. According to well-known biologists, not even Prigogine's self-organizing processes can help, because the organization that exists in life is dictated by genetic information, not by the environment.
- Generating the genetic code from chance takes enormous times, much longer than the age of the universe. Richard Dawkins has shown how time can be accelerated with *cumulative selection*, but implicit in there is an intelligent control system, not foreseen by the basic ideas of evolution.
- To explain the origin of life, and its evolution, it is plausible to think that it was guided in its appearance.

# CHAPTER 12

# CONCLUSIONS

*I do not believe in a personal God
and I have never denied this but have
expressed it clearly. If something is in
me which can be called religious then
it is the unbounded admiration for the
structure of the world so far as our
science can reveal it.*

— A. Einstein

In this book I have used the most current knowledge that physics, cosmology, and biology offer us to try to understand if this knowledge somehow gives indications that our universe and life were born by chance or if the case does not succeed to explain everything we observe. The basic question from which we started was: *"has science killed God?"*. With God we must not mean the personal god envisioned by religions, but an intelligent entity that was able to give the initial push to the origin of the universe and of life. A being who has created the laws that the universe follows and which have allowed life to form in at least one of its planets. The very existence of these laws, and their comprehensibility make us think that the universe is imbued with intelligence and that the idea of an initiating intelligence should not be discarded. Although there are laws that govern the universe, we only have a partial understanding of them. For example, we have a theory that describes the fundamental interactions that contains a series of constants whose values are not predicted by the theory, which must be added by hand and which remain outside our explanation. That theory provides three families for quarks and leptons while the matter that makes up the universe is made up only of the particles of a family. There is matter, namely dark matter, which is not predicted by that theory. We have a theory of space-time, but we don't understand what space and time really are. In the history of science there have been tremendous advances, in a few hundred years, so we should be hopeful that the future will bring us more knowledge that can fill the gaps in the knowledge we have today. Unfortunately, as Heisenberg showed there are limits to knowledge in the microscopic, while Kurt Godel showed that there are properties of numbers that are beyond our capabilities and that the whole system of mathematics cannot prove its consistency. The theorems demonstrated by Godel place limits on our knowledge: we will not be able to know everything about our universe, since mathematics is fundamental to understand the laws of nature. In other words, it seems that nature reveals itself in some of its features, allows us to know it in part, but keeps us away from total knowledge. There are other areas of physics that remind us of our limitations on knowledge: *catastrophe theory* or *deterministic chaos theory*. A typical example of catastrophe are earthquakes produced by relative movements between tectonic plates. These move slowly until at a certain point the sum of all these small movements causes a sort of break. Despite the studies on disasters, the theory of disasters does not allow us to make predictions. Continuous processes are easily modeled with the equations of physics, but when non-linearities come into play, we can no longer make predictions. An extreme case of non-linearity is chaos. Most systems are non-linear. As Lorentz showed in the 1960s, it is enough to have a simple system with *three degrees of freedom*, such as a simple double pendulum, for it to be chaotic. Examples of chaotic systems is the atmosphere; liquids under certain conditions have turbulent and chaotic behaviors. Contrary to what Laplace thought, the solar system is also a chaotic system over extremely long periods. One of the characteristics of chaotic systems is the *strong dependence on initial conditions*. What does it mean? If we take the simple case of the double pendulum, and drop the extremity from 1 m, it will show a certain evolution over time, but if we drop it from 1.000000000000000000000001 m, the evolution at some point will become different from the previous one.

Minor changes in initial conditions produce large changes in the behavior of chaotic systems. We usually speak of the so-called *butterfly effect*, term coming from a speech by Lorenz at a conference in 1972 "*Can the flapping of the wings of a butterfly in Brazil cause a tornado in Texas*". The butterfly effect, that is the extreme dependence of the behavior of a system on the initial conditions, was studied by Lorenz as early as 1962. Due to the dependence on the initial conditions, we will never know what will happen to the system over long periods. In other words, chaos places other limits on our knowledge. If we look at cosmology we do not know how the universe originated. We have seen that we have neither the theoretical nor the experimental tools to "take a look" at what happened at the time of the Big Bang. There are attempts to build the necessary physics, quantum gravity, but they are neither complete, nor do we know if it will be possible to create a theory that brings together gravity and quantum mechanics. There are models that using incomplete versions of this theory declare that the universe originated from nothing, but if we go to see what the nothingness of this model is, it is defined as the absence of space-time, but obviously the model must assume that physical laws exist. For the most part, physicists are "Platonic" that is, they believe that physical laws have an existence in themselves, not dependent on the universe. Hence the problem of who created them arises. In other words, our ideas on the origin of the universe should be cataloged as mere speculations. The Planck era, immediately following the Big Bang, remains a mystery because, as mentioned, we do not know the physics of that era. In the initial phase of the universe, all interactions had to be unified into one. This great unification remains only a theoretical prediction since our accelerators cannot generate the energies necessary to study that era.

There is also indirect evidence, contrary to its existence. After this era, the universe underwent an enormous expansion, inflation, which took the universe from dimensions of the order of $10^{-26}$ m to that of a soccer ball, in a fraction of a second. This phase is crucial to explaining some of the characteristics of our universe. Just remember that it was in the final part of this phase that the energy extracted from the vacuum gave rise to an enormous heating of the universe and therefore to the "condensation" of this energy into particles. In 2012, the Higgs boson was discovered which confirms the Higgs mechanism describing how elementary particles took on the mass we observe today. And yet, although there are several theories of inflation, no firm evidence, the *"smoking gun"*, of its existence has yet been found. Our knowledge of the early universe, at times earlier than $10^{-12}$ s, is based on speculations, but what happened next has been verified experimentally. From the period in which quarks and gluons were a boiling soup, up to the formation of stars and galaxies. The quarks came together in groups of three to form protons and neutrons. They did this in such a way that later protons and neutrons could give rise to atoms. For this to happen the charges of the electrons (defined as -1) had to be equal but of opposite sign to that of the protons (defined as +1). The latter are made up of quarks which therefore must have the right charges to constitute the charge of the protons. Matter is made up of up quarks, charged +2/3, and down quarks, charged, -1/3. A proton contains two up and one down quarks, therefore the sum of the charges of the two up and down quarks is exactly +1, the same charge as the electron, apart from the sign. Similarly, a neutron is made up of two down quarks and one up, and therefore has zero charge. This allowed atoms (hydrogen, helium, and some lithium) to form about three minutes after the Big Bang. This is another of those "coincidences", or pseudo-coincidences, of which we spoke in chapter 7, necessary for the construction of the universe we see. The work of building the universe was continued by gravity which has the right intensity to accumulate the gas, forming huge clouds whose collapse gave rise to nuclear fusion and the birth of stars, thanks to other "coincidences" of which we talked about in the chapter 7. The stars have "built" within them the heavy elements, precisely those necessary for life, which were then expelled in the supernova phase. Thus galaxies were born. Planets also formed around the stars and our planet was formed 4.5 billion years ago. The creation of the universe and everything that follows to date is studded with a multitude of "coincidences", or miracles depending on the point of view, without which the universe would not be what we know. If the density of the early universe had been slightly different (a factor less than one part in $10^{61}$) from the critical one, the universe would have expanded dramatically or would have collapsed immediately. If there hadn't been an asymmetry between matter and antimatter, the universe today would be full of photons and not stars. If the neutron masses had been slightly greater, the neutron-to-proton mass ratio would be different with the consequence of having more helium and less hydrogen with the consequence that reactions in primordial stars would not have been triggered. The universe would have remained dark and without heavy elements, without planets and without life. To the many "coincidences" mentioned in chapter 7, necessary to start from time zero and arrive at the formation of stars and galaxies, is added that of the cosmological constant, which began to prevail over gravity about four billion years ago, which has the right value so that the universe did not collapse or expand rapidly.

In the case of the cosmological constant, the fine-tuning must be 1 part in $10^{120}$. These are just a few examples that show how our universe is finely tuned. It seems that there is a universe control panel with a button for each constant of nature and that someone has played with it until they have all the right values to allow a universe like ours that allows life to exist. In other words, a solution to the problem of the fine-tuning of constants is that there is a designer, an intelligent mind who has taken everything into account in detail. If you don't believe in this possibility, we have few choices. One is that constants have the value they have by chance. Obviously this possibility is very unlikely given the great precision with which certain constants are regulated. Another pseudo-solution is based on the anthropic principle: the fundamental constants have the value they have because if they were not such we would not be here to observe the universe. Or if we use the strong version of the principle, the universe is such that sooner or later it must give rise to life. As we have seen, the weak version of the principle is basically a kind of tautology, while the strong one, understood as the existence of life as the final cause of the universe, takes us to a metaphysical, not scientific position. The ideas that constants are what they are by chance or by some form of the anthropic principle are rendered non-credible by the fact that, as calculated by Penrose, the particular state of the Big Bang dictated by entropy gives rise to extreme fine-tuning. : 1 in $10^{10^{123}}$.

The other possibility is based on the theory of the multiverse. If there are infinite universes beyond ours, in each of it, it is possible that the constants are different and it is therefore possible that there is a universe with the constants all adjusted as necessary. There are some areas of physics that "predict" the existence of a multiverse: quantum mechanics with its *many-worlds interpretation*, the theory of *chaotic inflation*, and *the theory of superstrings*.

The multiverse of quantum mechanics is not good for explaining the fine-tuning of constants because the values of the constants do not vary from one world to another. In chaotic inflation there is an eternal generation of universes all different from each other, with physical laws or at least constants that change from one to the other. In the superstring theory the extra compact dimensions correspond to false voids, different Universes, with different laws. So these two theories generate multiverses that can be used to explain the fine-tuning of constants. If one believes in the multiverse, the reason why our universe appears to be made specifically for life is just a matter of statistics. In the words of Paul Davies, we exist because we are the winners of a cosmic lottery. This point of view cancels the designer's need, at least as regards the explanation of the fine-tuning of the constants, but does not explain how the universe originated. The origin of the universe requires a mechanism or a designer and as mentioned before with the physics at our disposal we are not yet able to generate universes from "absolute nothing". Here the designer's idea peeps out again. It must also be said that for the multiverse to explain fine-tuning in an exhaustive manner, there must be a mechanism that generates the multiverse. Both superstring theory and chaotic inflation provide a mechanism that generates the multiverse. However a question arises: are these two theories that can generate the multiverse verified, and "reliable" theories? We have seen that they both have basic problems. Regarding the superstring theory, there is no evidence that it is a solid scientific theory. The huge number of compactifications, corresponding to distinct universes makes it an unverifiable theory, not falsifiable in the Popperian sense and therefore physically unscientific; a chameleontic theory that can adapt to any result. A theory that should be a theory of everything which is instead a theory of anything. In other words, the superstring theory should not even be considered as a "verifiable" mechanism for generating multiverses. We still have chaotic inflation. Also in this case there are several criticisms, the first of which, similarly to the case of string theory, is that it is not really falsifiable. Its parameters are too flexible for real experimental verification. Furthermore, the key proof, the "smoking gun" that confirms this theory is missing, namely the observation of primordial gravitational waves. So the second generation mechanism of the multiverse, based on chaotic inflation, is at least doubtful. If we are not sure of the existence of the multiverse, the fine-tuning of the constants tells us that a project must have existed. What about the origin of the universe then? Attempting to solve the problem by assuming that the universe did not have an origin, whether it is a cyclic universe or the like, does not eliminate the problem of the beginning because as shown mathematically by Vilenkin, these types of universe must also have an origin. The origin confronts us with the problem of how the universe originated. Is it possible to show that the universe originated from nothing, where by "nothing" we indicate the absence of space-time, energy, physical laws? No, it's not possible. In the first place we do not have a theory of quantum gravity that allows us to fully address the problem. With the methods used by Vilenkin it is possible to generate a universe of $10^{-35}$ m in size, which is then expanded by inflation. The structure that generates the universe is an initial "entity" not containing space-time which, by quantum tunneling, forms a universe. The problem is that the initial entity is not "nothing" and therefore *we have no way of generating a universe from nothing*. Once again, the idea of a designer who created a universe from nothing and then made it evolve by instilling the necessary laws of physics into the system peeps out.

Ultimately, there are no indications coming from physics and cosmology that science has "killed" God, indeed the idea of the project seems more likely than the one that everything originated by chance. Biology gives us other indications on the existence of a project and if science has killed God. The Earth originated about 4.5 billion years ago. At first its surface was incandescent, but it cooled quickly. It is thought that already 4.4 billion years ago there was already a crust. Life was formed between 3.8 and 3.4 billion years ago, after the so-called *late bombardment*, in which it was bombarded by a myriad of meteors, and asteroids. Primordial life forms appeared, including organisms that through photosynthesis changed the composition of the earth's atmosphere which began to contain a good amount of oxygen. Animal life first appeared in the oceans and then on dry land. After millions of years of evolution, the first hominids, Homo Sapiens and human consciousness appeared. How this all happened still remains a mystery in many respects. The study of the appearance of life on Earth and its evolution give indications on the question we asked ourselves, namely whether everything happened by chance or whether there is a project. We have seen that biologists have tried to prove that the existence of life occurred through random chemical processes that transformed non-life into life. If the initial part of the processes that led to life seems to take place automatically, such as the formation of amino acids, the way forward is very poorly understood. Life requires three aspects present simultaneously for its existence: *genetics, metabolism,* and *cellularity*. In an attempt to simplify the problem, proposals were made that took into account only one of these aspects. For example, the *RNA World* assumes that everything started from RNA and its enzymatic capabilities. The idea that the most fundamental of the three aspects was metabolism led to the hypothesis of the *iron-sulfur world*. The hypothesis that cellularity came first has led, for example, to the *world of lipids*. Despite all these attempts, even if we know more details concerning life origin, the goal of understanding the origin of life seems far away.

In the laboratory it is possible to obtain amino acids, and nucleotides, but in practice we have not clarified the origin of life on Earth. Several examples show that chance cannot make life out of basic building blocks. For example, to form a protein made up of 100 amino acids, we would have to bind them with peptide bonds. The probability of having 100 amino acids with peptide bonds is very low: 1 part in $10^{60}$. It has also been estimated that for a polypeptide to form in an amino acid soup left to itself, this soup should have the size of the universe. The biggest problem for the random formation of proteins from amino acids is the much greater time than the age of the universe. The probability of having 100 amino acids in the right order in a protein is 1 in $10^{130}$, and taking into account that life is made up of hundreds of thousands of proteins, the probability that they are formed by chance is $10^{40000}$. It was thought that self-organizing processes such as those described by Prigogine could simplify the transition from a non-living to a living system. Several biologists have shown that in reality this is not possible. Even if we know that life is based on order, it is not the order that arises from self-organizing processes. Life is organization that is directed by genetics. In a self-organization system such as a Raylegh-Benard cell, order is imposed by the environment. In the case of life, it comes from the system itself, from within. Decades of experiments have made researchers understand how enormous the problem is of explaining the origin of life, rather than leading them to a solution. If we pass from the level of proteins to that of DNA, we understand even better what are the difficulties that life implies. The origin of DNA and the mechanisms of translation of information to produce proteins is a problem far from being solved. DNA is a kind of very long word made up of 3.5 billion letters. As we have seen, typing it randomly on a keyboard takes about $10^{40}$ years to write 24 letters of Henry IV. The neo-Darwinists such as Richard Dawkins who in the past supported the thesis of the blind watchmaker, that is the idea of a blind and aimless evolution, realized with these trivial calculations that chance alone cannot build the huge variety of life forms and variations that fill the biosphere. The best method that Dawkins has found to accelerate evolution is the introduction of a *"cumulative selection"* system. The improvements made at every small step are verified and only the most efficient solutions are maintained. In this way, however, the idea of a blind and aimless evolution is distorted because intelligent control systems are introduced. The current situation regarding knowledge of the origin of life can be summarized as Stuart Kauffman of the Santa Fe Institute stated: *"Anyone who tells you that he or she knows how life started on the earth some 3.45 billion years ago is a fool or a knave. Nobody knows."*

An interesting thing to point out is that the probabilities discussed above show a close similarity to the fine-tuning of constants in physics. There would seem to be some sort of fine-tuning in the processes that led to life as well. Ultimately, to explain how life was born, one must accept the idea that chance alone does not build even "simple" molecules, and a form of intelligence is needed, a project at the basis of everything. The evolution gives similar indications, as seen in the previous simple calculations. Beyond the calculations, paleontological studies do not fit with the basic ideas of evolution.

In conclusion, the formation of a universe like ours is highly unlikely and the probability against the formation of life and its evolution up to the level of consciousness is enormously high. What surrounds us is due to a long series of highly improbable events. Our science, as already discussed, does not allow us to understand most of the key points that led to the appearance of the universe and of life. With our presence, the universe has achieved self-awareness: brute matter has evolved to consciousness and is now able to observe and partially understand itself. All this, with high probability, did not happen by chance, a form of intelligence guided or at least started the process. We can conclude that science did not kill God.

# INDEX

Lightning Source UK Ltd.
Milton Keynes UK
UKHW051815140922
408819UK00008B/194

9 789811 265587